MARCHON
THE WHITEHAVEN CHEMICAL WORKS

MARCHON
THE WHITEHAVEN CHEMICAL WORKS

ALAN W. ROUTLEDGE

TEMPUS

The Marchon Works in April 1954 occupied the site of the former Ladysmith Pit and Coke Works at Kells.

Frontispiece: Lord Schon of Whitehaven.

First published 2005

Tempus Publishing Limited
The Mill, Brimscombe Port,
Stroud, Gloucestershire, GL5 2QG
www.tempus-publishing.com

British Library Cataloguing in Publication Data.
A catalogue record for this book is available from the British Library.

ISBN 0 7524 3572 8

Typesetting and origination by Tempus Publishing Limited.
Printed in Great Britain.

Contents

David Basnett, the general secretary of the GMWU, is greeted by management and union representatives at Marchon. From left to right: Thompson Reed (union district organiser), Bert Harrington (personnel director), Martin Rowe (production director), Jim Smith (works convener GMWU), W. Rickleton (north region secretary GMWU), David Basnett, Ike Harrison (branch chairman), Jimmy Jardine (branch secretary).

Acknowledgements

The research needed for the production of this book has taken some considerable time and required the help and encouragement of several people and organisations. I am particularly indebted to the County Archive and Records Office at Whitehaven, who house the greater part of what remains of the Marchon papers; the Beacon, Whitehaven, who hold the photographic records of the company and to Rhodia, particularly Fred Proud, who kindly allowed me access to the whole of the archive before it was dispersed. Much use has been made of the two 'in house' magazines – *The Marchon News* and *The Albright World*.

I have received much encouragement from my friends Bob McConnell, Ray Devlin, Michael Moon and, not least, my wife Frances, who worked as a chemical analyst in the early years of the company.

Tank farm in front of S2 building. These were originally coal fired boilers and were used to store oleum, caustic soda, silicates and detergent alkylate.

Introduction

For more than half a century the tall chimneys of Marchon dominated the skyline above Whitehaven. Whilst they may not have been a pretty sight to some people, to those who worked in the factory, especially in the early days, the sight of the steam and smoke pouring out from them was a welcome sight. It meant their jobs were safe and at the end of the week they would pick up a decent pay packet.

The importance of Marchon Products Ltd to the local and national economy was nicely summed up in a speech given by the Prime Minister, Harold Wilson, at the 25th birthday celebrations of the company on 7 May 1965, when he said:

In helping to put the prosperity of West Cumberland beyond doubt, beyond danger, Marchon has made a great contribution, as I have said, not only to agriculture, not only to industry, not only to the saving of millions of dollars, but also to our nation's export drive. There cannot be many factories, in this country, who have a comparable record, in terms of production, which actually goes into export markets, and that is to say nothing of what is being done in overseas royalties, know-how, sales and the rest, to other countries who have followed in the wake of the pioneering efforts of the scientists of Whitehaven.

A remarkable endorsement of the policies of Frank Schon, Fred Marzillier and their team of fellow directors and of the efforts of the local workforce.

The commitment and effort put in by everyone on the Marchon site brought great success for the company and more and more jobs for the people of the town. The permanent workforce had reached 2,350 by the late 1960s with several hundred more contracting jobs, while new plants were built. The Labour governments of Clem Atlee and Hugh Gaitskell provided much of the funding for the early expansion. Such government help was less forthcoming when the Conservatives returned to power and, in order to keep the expansion going, Marchon were left with little alternative other than to merge with Albright and Wilson Ltd in 1955.

Marchon's requirements for phosphate rock led to some development of Whitehaven harbour. Later, plans to accommodate vessels of up to 30,000 tons capacity were drawn up after a great deal of investigation. These developments did not come to fruition for a number of reasons outside Marchon's control.

Over the years Marchon and A&W Ltd invested steadily in new production facilities overseas – Italy, France, Spain, Canada, South Africa, the USA, Malaya, Singapore, the Philippines and many other places. These ventures all took business and therefore production and jobs away from Whitehaven.

By 1967 A&W Ltd were looking to move phosphorous production to Canada, and they also appointed American management consultants to advise them on the organisation and management of the company. Despite protests by Frank Schon, the Canadian venture was pushed through and, in the implementation of the managerial changes demanded by the consultants, it became clear that there was no place for Frank Schon in the new set up. Schon accordingly resigned.

These events were the turning point in A&W's, and therefore Marchon's, fortunes and in order to keep the company afloat, following serious losses in Canada, they borrowed heavily from Houston-based Tenneco Inc. and by 1975 had been taken over by them. Despite the Americanisation of the company and some investment by them, particularly in the USA and Canada, but also in Whitehaven, profits in the UK were not up to the levels Tenneco expected. Disillusioned with the financial returns on their investment, they sold the company's UK and European sites back to the A&W Ltd management.

Things went from bad to worse and A&W Ltd sold out to the French company Rhodia in 2000, who systematically closed down the plants at Whitehaven after taking the business to France. They then sold the remains of the detergent business to the American company Huntsman who, in turn, moved the rest of the business and the customer base to other locations and closed the site for good in June 2005.

All these events form the basis of the Marchon story, which is told in words and photographs over the next hundred pages or so. I hope the reader finds memories of happier times at the big factory on the hill and that it serves as a permanent reminder of the company which contributed so much to both Whitehaven's and the nation's economic well-being.

Alan W. Routledge
March 2005

one

The Early Days
1939–1949

The old cottage at Hensingham which was used by Marchon as offices and for production in 1940.

On 6 December 1939 Marchon Products was registered in London as a Limited Company, with a capital value of £1,000, by partners Martha Tablin and Lionel Morris with Harold Wolf Fisher acting as company secretary. Mr Franz Schon was taken on by the partners as general manager and paid £500 for his goodwill and business contacts. He used that money to buy out Miss Tablin on 13 December 1939. At the same time Lionel Morris sold his 500 shares to Mr George G. Underwood. Fred Marzillier was appointed managing director on 5 February 1940, after purchasing 490 of George Underwood's shares.

Schon attended all board meetings and was paid as a member of the board, although he was not officially appointed as a director until 19 April 1945. The new company operated from No. 4 Cullum Street in the city of London, but these buildings were flattened by Hitler's bombs. After a short stay at Charterhouse Buildings they were bombed out again and the company moved to Whitehaven in 1940.

At Whitehaven they moved into a small dwelling house at Hensingham. A couple of months later three condemned cottages nearby were used as stores and the company began to manufacture and sell its first firelighters in partnership with Mrs Miriam Bailey.

At the same time Marchon began to market chemicals for use as raw materials in the detergents industry. One of the company's first customers was a nationally known producer of toiletries based in London whose works had been requisitioned by the government for the manufacture of aircraft parts. In May 1941 Marchon began to manufacture some of the company's products and in order to cope with an increasing workload they acquired property in the town, near the market, and it was here that the first chemical processing began.

The Cumbria Trading Co. Ltd was registered on 25 March 1942, with offices and works at the Guinea Warehouse, in the Newtown. This new company had just one director – Harold

One of several warehouses in Ripton Lane, behind Swingpump Lane, similar to those used by Marchon between 1940 and 1943.

Wolf Fisher, the Marchon company secretary. They immediately engaged Mr Otto Secher as technical manager.

Marchon soon dissolved their partnership for the manufacture of firelighters with Mrs Bailey and paid her a sum of £150 in cash on 9 April 1942, with three further monthly payments of £50. They made royalty agreements with Cumbria Trading for the manufacture of firelighters and washing powders by the 'secret processes belonging to Frank Schon and Fred Marzillier'. Royalties on firelighters were ⅚ per gross produced and sold and for powders, 10 per cent of the value of the net sales.

Manufactured from a mixture of fat, naphthalene and sawdust, firelighters became a relatively large business, bringing in the bulk of the company's income, all of which was carefully re-invested. The company then leased further premises in Swing Pump Lane from Mrs Isobella Brannon at £52 per quarter and on 25 January they engaged their first chemist – Dr W.S. Kewish.

In January 1943 they also purchased a warehouse and cottage in Ribton Lane from Mr Ramsey for £1,250. Later in 1943 Marchon took the step which would take them from a cottage industry to chemical manufacturers of international standing, when they made their final move to new premises – the disused tar plant at Ladysmith Pit near Kells.

Marchon purchased seven acres of land and some of the tar plant's old buildings, which were converted to chemical manufacture. New buildings were added when needed. Most of the conversion work was carried out with the help of their neighbours, the privately owned Cumberland Coal Co., who also supplied Marchon with electricity, steam and water at a very good price.

A second sister company – Solway Chemicals Ltd – was formed on 14 December 1943, the directors of which were: Fred Marzillier, Frank Schon, William Sunner (a Whitehaven solicitor),

Arnold Waterhouse and Harry Greenwood (former directors of Dunn Bros, Manchester), and Frank Brayshaw from Baildon in Yorkshire. William Sumner was appointed company secretary and the biggest shareholder – Frank Brayshaw – was voted managing director, a position he held until 1946.

The main products of Solway Chemicals were liquid fertilisers and the toothpaste foaming agent sodium lauryl sulphate, which was spray dried outside the company on a contract basis. It was not until 1945 that Solway Chemicals installed the Kestner spray driers in S2 building. Solway Chemicals also developed one of the companies most profitable products – rayon spinning oil.

During the war years the company's activities were restricted to the manufacture of firelighters and some detergent intermediates. All raw materials were bought in, including fatty alcohols. The other raw materials – sulphuric acid and caustic soda – were brought to the site. Manufacturing facilities were rudimentary, consisting of just a couple of lead-lined vessels which were filled by hand and the strong acids and alkalis which were added to the mixture via large earthenware jugs filled from glass carboys.

Maintenance to the plant was carried out by people who worked during the day for other companies, such as the Gas Co., and who were prepared to come in the evenings and at weekends to give the new chemical company a hand. This situation arose because most workmen at this time were away in the armed forces or in reserved occupations. All of the company's directors took an active part in the manufacturing operations and throughout the early years the firelighters business was the major contributor to the profits. The early developments at the Ladysmith site were vital, laying the foundations for the later, greater growth of the company. Not only did they create the nucleus of the management team but they also provided all of the early funding of the company.

It was during these formative years that lasting local connections were forged, and contact was made with government officials whose aim was the economic regeneration of West Cumberland. The company found a particularly good friend in Jack Adams, later Lord Adams of Ennerdale, who was then chairman and secretary of the West Cumberland Industrial Development Co.

The end of the Second World War released a number of chemists and engineers from the ordnance factories at Drigg and Sellafield, who found employment at Marchon and became members of the senior management team including: A.C. Halfpenny, Bernard B. Dugan and William Colquitt. Demobilisation added to the available workforce and the 'Marchon Team' began to evolve. Bill Hampshire and Bob Dickie arrived in September 1947 and were employed as senior chemists. In addition to manpower, buildings and equipment became available from the local TNT factories, some of which were acquired by Marchon and transferred to the Ladysmith site, where the most important of the buildings eventually became Lab 3, S4 and S5. At the same time two Babcock and Wilcox steam boilers were purchased from a Royal Navy ship, which had been used as a brewery for the forces overseas. Marchon then became self-sufficient in the production of steam power.

During the immediate post-war years some of the very first soap substitutes to reach the UK market were produced in S4 building. Although 'in fashion' for a short while, whilst real soap was still hard to find, that most discerning of customers – the housewife – did not immediately take to the newfangled washing powders. The tradename 'Spel' was registered by Cumbria Trading on 6 May 1948 and later that year B.B. Duggan and the newly-arrived Albert Taylor applied for Marchon's first patent for improved detergent formulations.

Arthur Clare Halfpenny and Bernard Baron Dugan were appointed directors of Marchon Products Ltd on 1 January 1949 and at the same time Michael Eugene Dufaye was appointed

Mrs Hilda McAleese, Marchon's first full-time employee. John Eilbeck was working for the company earlier than Hilda but on a part-time basis.

A young process worker blocking firelighters at the Ladysmith Works. The firelighters looked like big blocks of chocolate but stank of naphthalene.

The blocks of six firelighters were packed in cellophane bags and wrapped, ready for sale. This work was invariably done by female workers.

Bernard Baron Dugan, sales director of
Marchon Products Ltd, c.1949

Analyst Janet Shilholme checks a
burette reading whilst carrying out
the measurement of the percentage of
active matter in a sample of shampoo.
Note the Manesty distilled water unit
top right. The laboratories used a great
deal of distilled water every day.

The railway sidings at Marchon in the late 1940s with tank farms 1, 2 and 3. Also in the picture are, from left to right: S5; Lab 3; S4 and S2 buildings.

sales manager; James C. Evans replaced Bill Colquitt as production manager and Alexander Lindsay was appointed chief engineer.

In addition to firelighters and some shampoo and detergent intermediates, fatty esters were produced in S1 (one of the original Ladysmith buildings), the most important of which – glycerol mono-strearate – was used in the pharmaceutical and the food industries as an emulsifier in creams and lotions and in the production of artificial whipped cream, ice-cream and as a bread whitener. Other esters were made for use in textile spinning oils and as plasticisers for PVC.

Towards the end of 1948, the board of directors had a fundamental decision to make – should the company become a detergent raw materials manufacturer or should they go all the way and sell their own brands of packed detergent powders direct to the nation's shopkeepers? It was a very difficult decision to make and getting it right was vital for the future of chemicals manufacture in Whitehaven. Marchon decided to concentrate on the manufacture of both detergent intermediates and finished powders to a point where they could be marketed by other companies.

Although the war years had brought the development of synthetic detergents in Europe to a halt, this was not the case in the USA, where considerable progress had been made. It was a situation which led to Frank Schon and Arthur Halfpenny making a visit to the USA in 1948, where they quickly confirmed that the policy laid down by Marchon was the right one. The information garnered in the USA showed that the pace and scale of development of the detergents business would be dictated entirely by their acceptance by the chief user – the housewife.

Clearly the domestic market was the one to aim for and in order to win it detergents would have to be designed and manufactured not as a substitute for, but as a noticeable improvement over, soap.

Lab 3 building with the newly built S6 stores in the background.

During 1949 the first major contract to manufacture packed household detergents and low-salt bases for toothpaste and shampoos for the American soap manufacturer Colgate, Palmolive and Peet Inc. was agreed. This entailed enlarging the detergent drier and installing modern, state of the art, packaging machinery in S4 building. The initial contract was for three years and in order to capitalise the necessary plant improvements, Marchon sold half a million shares in the company to Colgate.

The West Cumberland Industrial Development Co. was an immense help to the company and they gave Marchon every encouragement, in particular by helping them to obtain essential licences of every description. These were needed on an almost daily basis at a time when the treasury held the nation's finances in a stranglehold. Moreover, during 1949 material help was given by the provision, under a long-term lease, of 75,000sq.ft of factory space and an office block of 12,000sq.ft. These facilities came at a vital time in the company's development and proved to be the springboard for even greater expansion.

For the first time outside finance was sought and acquired under the authority of HM Treasury through the Industrial and Commercial Finance Corporation Ltd, who became minority shareholders in Marchon after providing some £300,000 at 4 per cent interest per annum, in return for some of the shares held by Frank Schon, Fred Marzillier, Otto Secher, Billy Dugan and Arthur C. Halfpenny, together with a further 1,964,000 new shares.

The new factory space came in the form of a building which housed the office block, the first aid centre, the staff and works canteens, the tumbling and needling plant and S6 stores. These facilities were opened on 8 January 1949 by the Chancellor of the Exchequer, Sir Stafford Cripps.

The Marchon Works consisted of process buildings S1, S2 and S4, (S5 still an empty shell); Lab 3; S6 stores and office block; a new boiler house; the firelighter department and an

Shift chemist Jimmy Kerr and process foreman Tom Nicholson discuss the Ph of a batch of shampoo with research chemist Austin Sowerby.

engineering shop complete with electricians, fitters, joiners, pipe-fitters, plumbers, riggers and welders. The company was able to carry out its own maintenance and some small scale manufacture of process plant.

The growth of business during 1947–49 allowed the company to build up its administration section and its laboratory facilities and staff. The sales department was carefully set up and great emphasis was placed on export trade. Leading the way in sales were Billy Dugan, sales director; Mike Dufaye, export sales manager; and Otto Secher, in charge of firelighter and packed detergent sales.

During this period close contacts were made with the major soap manufacturers, some of whom purchased finished detergents, manufactured and packaged by Marchon in their own packets, whilst others preferred to buy raw materials and intermediate products.

All raw material requirements were purchased in 1949, including detergent grade phosphates, hydrocarbons and fatty alcohols, most of which were imported into the United Kingdom.

Marchon were processors of intermediates rather than manufacturers of basic chemicals and, to secure a future for the company and its workforce, a great deal more had to be done. Fortunately, the directors of the company were aware that bringing in every single raw material to Whitehaven was a costly business – too costly for the company to survive. The cost of moving thousands of tons of raw materials into Whitehaven and then moving even more tons of product out to all parts of the world ate too deeply into the profit margin. Indeed, the very reason for Marchon's existence in Whitehaven was the town's remoteness from the rest of the UK and Europe, and particularly Adolf Hitler. Soon after the war that same remoteness became a major handicap. A new plan was needed, one to be agreed and implemented over the next five years.

Glass-lined ester pots EPs 1, 2 and 3 in S1 building. They were used to manufacture esters of glycerine and fatty acids for the food and cosmetics industries.

Sir Stafford Cripps, the Chancellor of the Exchequer, officially opens the new offices and S6 stores in 1948 in the presence of Jack Adams, Frank Schon and Fred Marzillier.

Frank Schon and Arthur Halfpenny aboard the *Queen Mary* leaving New York in 1949. They visited America to investigate the detergents business.

Technical service chemist Tom Smith checks out the quality of a sample of liquid detergent in the late 1940s.

Continuous plant charge hand Oliver Christian makes a quick adjustment to the Ph of the neutraliser by adding a shovel full of soda ash (washing soda).

Otto Secher, sales director of Marchon Products Ltd and later chairman of the Marchon Division.

Frank Schon and Billy Dugan meet a couple of visitors who have just flown into the Workington Steel Works airstrip from the continent.

A block and tackle was the common method of lifting drums of raw materials into a process building in the 1940s and '50s.

An experimental, continuous sulphonation plant in which tallow fatty alcohol was reacted with oleum (super strong sulphuric acid) in large water cooled glass spheres. The acid and alcohol were fed onto a spinning disc which threw the mixture to the walls of the vessel where it was instantly cooled. The neutralised product was used in low foam detergents.

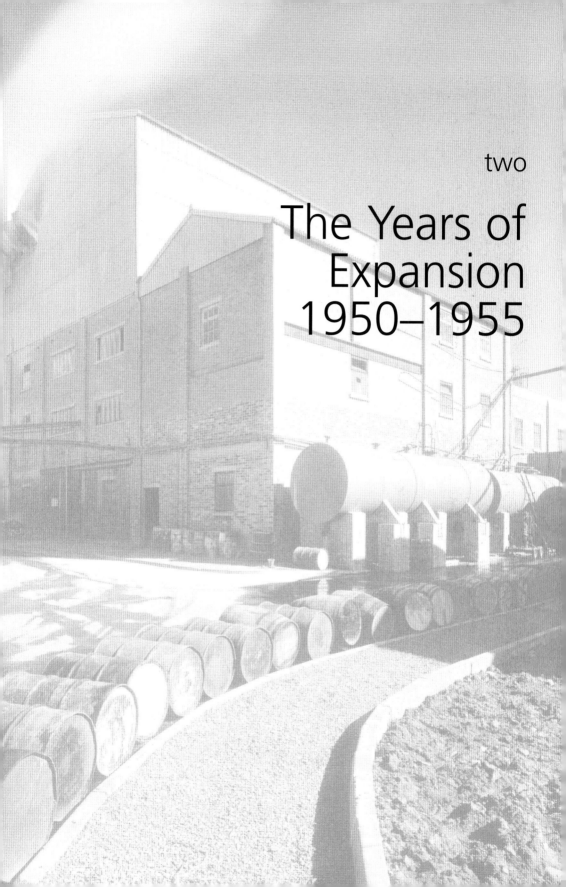

two

The Years of Expansion 1950–1955

Above left: The bottom of SD4 where the detergent powder left the drier. The hot air inlet fan is on the right.

Above right: The packing room in S4 building running on Colgate's detergent powder FAB. The packets were filled and sealed automatically and checked for weight and quality.

The plan conceived by the directors for the future of Marchon was a simple one – the company would manufacture, at the Kells site, as many of its raw material requirements as possible. Finance for these developments came from a number of different sources including insurance companies and the Industrial and Commercial Finance Corporation Ltd but by far the largest amount came from the government through the Development Areas Treasury Advisory Committee, which in Marchon's case meant the West Cumberland Industrial Development Co.

Organics

The Cumbria Trading Co. made an agreement with Firelighter Developments Ltd for the manufacture of white firelighters based on a paraffin/resin mixture. A new plant was built for their manufacture and after running both types of firelighter manufacture in tandem for a while the original type was phased out.

By 1952, S5 was being used as a process building, for the production of high active shampoo and toothpaste foaming agents. A little while later a vessel and ancillary equipment was installed for the manufacture of lauric isopropanolamide, a fatty material used as a foam booster in shampoos and bubble baths.

During the early 1950s much research work was carried out in Lab 3 into the sulphation of fatty alcohol ethoxylates for use in high performance shampoos, and the company decided to carry out the ethoxylation process on site. There was some space between S5 and the main road for the unit which consisted of a reactor and ethylene oxide storage vessel. The sausage-shaped vessels were set in an area surrounded by a thick blast wall and the contents of both vessels were kept under a blanket of pure nitrogen and in order to keep them cool, cold water was sprayed over them constantly.

Approximately 90 per cent of the shampoos sold in the UK were then based on primary fatty alcohols and their derivates and with over 90 per cent of the shampoos sold in the country being produced in Whitehaven the need to find a local supply for these alcohols was of paramount importance. After due consideration the company's technical staff elected to use high pressure hydrogenation technology as their route to fatty alcohols.

The plant was designed for maximum flexibility and could make fatty alcohols from a variety of raw materials including esters of natural oils and fats and from natural fatty acids. The plant consisted of the following five sections:

Esterification
High pressure hydrogenation
Hydrogen generation
Catalyst manufacture
Distillation

Approximately one ton each of lauryl alcohol and lauric acid were esterified in a large column to produce two tons of lauryl laurate, which was then reacted with hydrogen in a series of autoclaves at a pressure of 300 atmospheres and at a temperature of 300 degrees centigrade. This yielded two tons of lauryl alcohol and, after distillation, one ton of the product alcohol was recycled to the esterification column, thus only half of the product alcohol found its way for use elsewhere in the factory.

Pure hydrogen was produced by the electrolysis of a solution of caustic soda in a Knowles Diaphragm Cell. The direct electrical current needed for this process was supplied from mercury arc rectifiers.

When the plant was opened by Sir Henry Tizzard on 22 June 1954, it was Marchon's first venture into high pressure technology. At the opening ceremony Frank Schon had the following to say:

The new high pressure plant is not a particularly large one as far as this kind of technical equipment goes. Much larger units with similar features are customary in the manufacture of some synthetic organic chemicals. However I hasten to claim a special feature for our plant – its flexibility. Allowing for the training of expert personnel, it should be possible, within a year, to produce higher molecular alcohols at a rate of 4,000 tons per annum. The applications of fatty alcohols are extensive; they and their derivatives are used in the textile, leather, pharmaceutical, plastics, synthetic rubber and many other industries.

The alcohol plant was built by Marchon's own 400-strong engineering section and when it was opened it had cost just under £500,000 to build. The plant was managed by Martin D. Rowe assisted by Stan Wilson. Shift managers included Gavin Barr, Harry Easdon, Jimmy Hayes and Ernie Sanderson, and the special operating conditions of the plant required an expert team of shift engineers – Cyril Gordon, John Greggain, George McKelvie and Jimmy Martin.

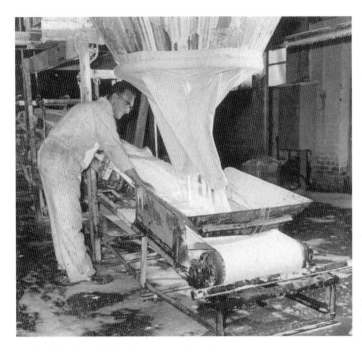

Shift foreman Bill Rothery checks the appearance of the dried powder leaving SD4.

Inorganics

The new plan for the development of the Whitehaven site demanded the manufacture of the essential detergent raw material – sodium tripolyphosphate. For this, phosphoric acid was needed, which was produced by attacking the phosphate rock with sulphuric acid in large digester vessels. The reaction produced a mixture of gypsum and crude green acid which was separated from the slurry by filtration, the crude acid was then concentrated. For use in detergents the acid also needed a degree of purification. 'The Wet Process', as it was called, became Marchon's chosen manufacturing process.

Tripolyphosphate (STPP) was produced by neutralising the acid with either caustic soda or anhydrous sodium carbonate (soda ash), followed by drum drying and roasting in a large rotary kiln to give a detergent grade STPP.

Up to then Marchon had purchased all of its detergent phosphate requirements from a number of sources, including Perry & Hope Ltd of Nitshill, Glasgow. In order to meet the Marchon requirement, they needed to invest, and in January 1951 they sought a loan of £60,000 from Marchon, who received shares in return. Marchon commissioned a report into the activities of Perry & Hope and soon learned the worst.

Mr S. Campbell-Johnson and Mr W. Wright resigned their directorships in Perry & Hope and were replaced by Alec Lindsay on 30 September 1951. The new board of directors decided to cease trading at the earliest possible moment and further changes to the management of P & H occurred in March 1952 when Peter Baines replaced Mr J.C. Stewart. On 26 October 1954 an extraordinary meeting of Perry & Hope Ltd was held in Whitehaven and the company was wound up.

The phosphates plant at Kells was the first to be constructed south of Ladysmith Pit Lane and, when opened, was known as F1 and was capable of producing some 20,000 tons of P_2O_5 per annum, in the form of detergent grade phosphoric acid, which was converted into 22,500 tons of tripolyphosphate per annum. The plant was managed by John Welsh and Patrick Quinn.

S6 blending and tumbling unit in which powder shampoos were carefully blended to a standard quality.

Joe Young, foreman of the tumbling and needling plants, examines a sample of high active sodium lauryl sulphate needles. These were produced to pharmaceutical quality.

Sulphuric acid was, and to a large extent still is, one of the most important raw materials in the world's chemical industry, always in demand and always in short supply. In the early 1950s more than 75 per cent of the UK's production was based on imported elemental sulphur coming mostly from America. When Marchon developed a need for sulphur the United Nations were fighting a war in Korea which led to a world wide shortage of sulphur and they were driven to look at other manufacturing methods and, during 1951, HM government pushed the company hard to find an alternate process.

Although the company did not know it, they were sitting on top of a considerable field of anhydrite and it was only after Jack Adams told the directors about the geology of the area that the project took off.

ICI Ltd had been operating a process at Billingham using anhydrite as the starting block since 1930 and were willing to sell the know-how for the process, but only at a price that Frank Schon and his co-directors considered to be exorbitant. They were aware that a firm in Lintz, Austria, was about to start making sulphuric acid by the anhydrite route and Frank Schon set off immediately for his former home country. Here he placed a series of advertisements in the local press offering 'glorious technical opportunities' for those who knew the acid process. Then, armed with a hatful of replies, he asked for, and got, an interview with the managing director of the Lintz Co. He admitted that it was he who had placed the adverts and if it could be avoided he would prefer not to denude the company of its technical strength, and if pointed in the right direction to obtain the information so urgently needed, he would destroy all the replies he had received.

Schon was then introduced to Dr. H.H. Kuehne, a former managing director of IG Farben and the co-inventor of the process, and he became the consultant to Solway Chemicals Ltd. The shareholders of Solway chemicals were Marchon Products Ltd and the Industrial and Commercial Finance Corporation Ltd, who had already co-operated with financial assistance in the development of the Whitehaven Chemical Works. The Development Area Treasury Advisory

Above left: The refrigeration plant behind the old boiler house. Recycled cold water was the main coolant used on the factory and refrigeration was necessary to keep the circulating water cold.

Above right: Laboratory assistant Pat Scurr carried out daily dishwashing tests on detergent samples. The dishes were soiled with a standard mixture of fat, grease, egg and protein to ensure a fair test of cleaning power.

Committee's interests in the affairs of Solway Chemicals Ltd were discussed in a debate in the House of Commons on Wednesday 19 March 1952. On the basis of a debenture issue, a working capital was provided by DATAC, under Section 4 of the Distribution of Industry Act, 1945.

At the inauguration ceremony on 24 May 1952, when Jack Adams dug out the first sod of earth on the Solway site, Frank Schon noted 'It has taken a great deal of time to negotiate all the basic agreements and to obtain the necessary licenses.' He continued, 'These preliminary negotiations are now complete and I can now tell you all about the project. We estimate it will take between two and two and a half years to complete the construction work and when the plant is in operation it should give an opportunity for quite a number of school leavers to train in technical processing. Ultimately, as many as 300 process workers may find employment on the plant'.

The first stage in the process – the anhydrite mine – was opened on 11 January 1955 by Sir Robert Chance the Lord Lieutenant of Cumberland, with the sulphuric acid plant coming on stream on 14 November of the same year. The new complex was officially opened by HRH Prince Phillip, the Duke of Edinburgh, and by the end of the year Marchon was producing more than 100,000 tons of acid at a cost of about £8 per ton and a similar quantity of Portland grade cement. Savings in transport costs for sulphuric acid alone would pay off the plant in a just a few years.

A process worker taking a sample of alkylolamide from a reactor in S5. The reactor was manufactured by Marchon's engineers from an old absorption tower which came from Sellafield. It was far from ideal, being long and narrow, but did the job.

The merger with Albright and Wilson Ltd

During November 1955, the Birmingham-based chemical company, Albright and Wilson Ltd announced that it had merged with Marchon Products Ltd but in effect A&W had purchased Marchon Products Ltd, Solway Chemicals Ltd, and The Cumbria Trading Co Ltd. In making its announcement A&W stated 'it had agreed to buy, for £2,617,000, the entire share capital not at present held by Marchon. The shares thus purchased by A&W included all those held by The Industrial & Commercial Development Co., Courtaulds Ltd, Colgate, Palmolive & Peet Inc. and a number of insurance companies.

To finance the package and provide for further expansion, A&W planned to raise about £4.5 million of new money by a rights issue. The merger came about because Marchon was unable to raise the additional capital it needed from its traditional sources.

In a statement issued at the time, speaking on behalf of the Marchon board Frank Schon said 'For some time now it has been apparent that, due to the company's rapid expansion, its ordinary share capital had become completely out of gear in relation to the total capital employed in the business. In the past it has been the practice to finance expansion at Marchon mainly by ploughing back all profits, but it became necessary to find additional capital in the form of loans, particularly for the Solway sulphuric acid and cement complex.'

During 1950/51 Marchon decided to manufacture sulphuric acid from anhydrite. The project was inaugurated by Jack Adams on 24 May 1952, when he cut the first sod of earth at the Solway site.

The Marchon site in 1954, showing the full extent of the factory at the time. Note the first phosphate plant (F1) under construction.

Process worker Harold Clifford checks on the strength of the phosphoric acid by means of a hydrometer which gave the specific gravity of the acid in degrees Twaddle.

The capital required for such further expansion could not be raised without enlarging the financial basis of Marchon–Solway. To attempt to do this by the issue of additional ordinary share capital presented the directors with a variety of difficulties. As a consequence, the problem was solved by the incorporation of Marchon–Solway into an existing organisation which had the facilities then lacking at Marchon.

Following the merger, the management of Marchon–Solway continued to operate the company, which still traded under its own name, with Frank Schon also serving on the board of Albright and Wilson Ltd. Thus began a relationship which, in the long run, would be fraught with difficulties even though, by the end of the period, phosphate production had been doubled, sulphuric acid manufacture started and the permanent workforce had grown to 1,447 men and women.

The drum-dried phosphate was converted into detergent grade tripolyphosphate by heating it to a high temperature in these rotary kilns.

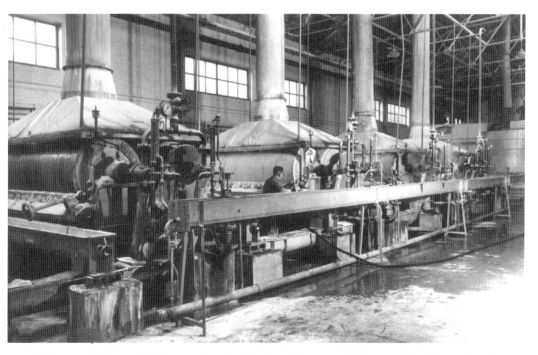

After neutralisation and before roasting, the phosphate liquor was dried on a series of steam heated drums.

Part of the crowd of laboratory staff and office workers waiting to greet Prince Phillip, the Duke of Edinburgh, in 1955. Amongst the spectators are Frances Walters, Cilla Colquitt, Mary Warwick, Janet Shilholme and Betty Coid.

The sulphuric acid complex at Solway was opened on 24 November by HRH Prince Phillip, the Duke of Edinburgh, seen here with Frank Schon.

Right: During his visit the Duke of Edinburgh went underground at the Solway anhydrite mine and is seen here with the mine general manager, Ernie Charlton, and works director, Arthur Halfpenny.

Below: Unlike the local coal mines, where the seams are low and gassy, the anhydrite seam could reach 25ft thick and was free of methane. The mine had many miles of roadways, several yards wide and up to 20ft high, which allowed the extracted rock to be moved by bulldozer and dumper truck.

Opposite above: The anhydrite was roasted in large rotary kilns to produce sulphur dioxide gas and cement clinker. This photograph shows No.1 kiln under construction. The upper kiln was used to roast the rock whilst the lower kiln was used to cool the cement clinker.

Opposite below: Anhydrite mine workers travelled into the mine by man-trains running down an inclined drift until the men were 450ft below ground. The product was raised by conveyor belt in a sister drift.

Right: After drilling, the bore-holes in the anhydrite were packed with explosive, fused and wired, then fired from a safe distance. Here a deputy/shot firer fuses up the 'jelly' prior to inserting it into a bore-hole.

Below: A general view of the old fatty alcohol complex with the phosphates plant on the left.

From left to right: Lord Lonsdale, Sir Henry Tizzard (who officially opened the plant), Jack Adams and Frank Schon standing beside one of a pair of four stage hydrogen compressors which raised the pressure of the gas to 4,500lb per square inch.

The heart of the alcohol process was the high pressure unit. From left to right: the paste heater, the hydrogen heater, the first and second reactors, the hot separator, the cold separator and the hydrogen knock-out pots.

The copper chromite catalyst plant showing the copper dissolving tower and nitric oxide absorption tower. To the right are the fatty alcohol plant distillation and esterification columns.

Hydrogen was produced by the electrolysis of caustic soda solution in a series of Knowles diaphragm cells. The resultant hydrogen was fed to a large gas holder and the oxygen was bled to the atmosphere.

The fatty alcohol distillation and esterification columns under construction. The large cylindrical vessel below was the distillation unit boiler, where the fatty alcohols were vaporised under high vacuum.

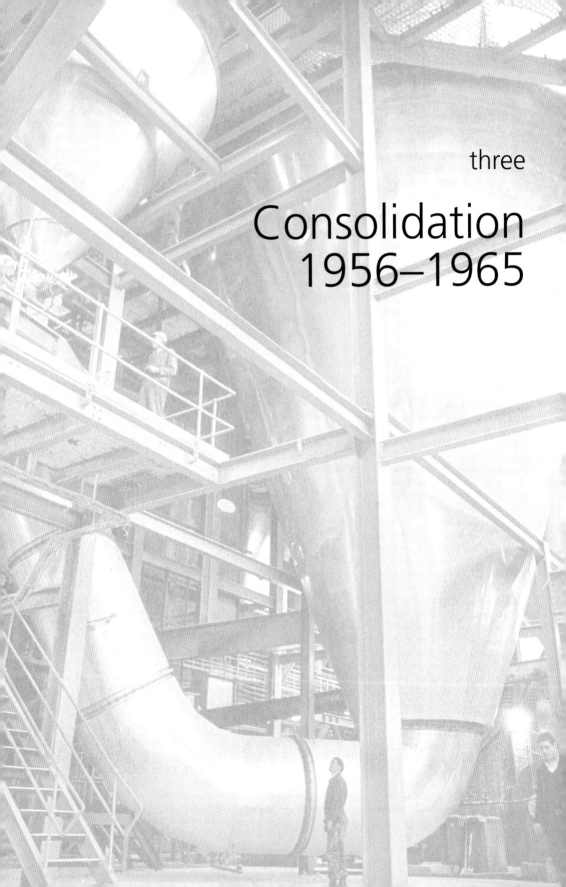

three

Consolidation
1956–1965

The next ten years were about consolidation and yet more expansion, not only in terms of the existing plant and facilities but also of new processes and products which required completely different manufacturing equipment. Most of these new processes were on the organics side of the business.

Organics

After signing an agreement with Thomas Hedley & Co. to manufacture and sell detergent compositions under patent licenses, Marchon erected its first plant for the manufacture of methyl esters of coconut oil by the process of trans-esterification. The process had been developed by Dr Adolf Koebner and his team of research chemists.

Methyl ester replaced lauryl laurate in the hydrogenation process resulting in a considerably greater yield of fatty alcohol. The ester could also be used for the manufacture of alkylolamides, which were used as foam boosters in detergent and shampoo formulations. This latter process led to the end of alkylolamide manufacture in S1.

For some time Marchon had been looking at the manufacture of methacrylate monomers and polymers based on their range of fatty alcohols. The polymers were used in motor lubricating oils where they acted as viscosity modifiers. As a result of a considerable amount of experimental work and close co-operation with Wakefield Ltd, the makers of the Castrol range of motor oils, a pilot plant was constructed to finalise the process. The full-scale plant was opened in early 1957, after a short delay due to an engineering strike, and when the plant was handed over to the production department Bob Southward became the plant manager. The oil additive plant (OAP) and its products became one of the company's most successful and profitable projects. Apart from sales to Castrol, much of the production was sold to Eastern Europe, particularly the Czech Republic and Poland.

No sooner had the OAP been handed over to the production department than the construction of another organics plant was completed and ready for commissioning. The project was described in the trade press, during April 1958, in the following terms, 'The Eltesol range is a series of aromatic sulphonates manufactured in commercial quantities.' The products were used in the detergent and paper industries as wetting agents and also in the foundry industry as catalysts for resin products.

A serious fire occurred in the bottom of the fatty alcohol distillation column on 5 September 1960. Such was the intensity of the heat generated, the steel shell of the column softened and could no longer support itself. The column collapsed, luckily falling straight down the road, missing most of the storage vessels and a road tanker loading up with fatty alcohol for delivery to a customer. The plant was out of commission for three weeks during which time the engineering department built and erected a new column.

In the late 1950s a large pilot plant was built to sulphonate detergent alkylate using SO_3 gas, which was bought in initially and later supplied from the Solway acid plant. This unit gave the company much needed flexibility in the sulphation and sulphonation processes of both alkylate and fatty alcohols.

Such was the demand for sulphated fatty alcohol products, both at home and overseas, that during 1962 the company decided to increase fatty alcohol production to 20,000 tons per annum. In 1963, a new plant was designed and constructed by the German engineering firm Lurgi GMBH using their own patented process. Instead of using methyl esters as feed stock,

Members of the Marchon Products Ltd board of directors in 1955. From left to right: Peter Baines (company secretary), Bernard Dugan, Frank Schon, Fred Marzillier, Arthur Halfpenny and Otto Secher.

The methyl ester plant under construction in 1956, with the copper chromite catalyst plant behind. Outside the plant waiting to be installed on the open gantry are the large reaction vessels used in the trans-esterification process.

By the 1950s, Marchon had a presence at many trade fairs across the world. This is a typical Marchon trade stand, staffed by Whitehaven-based chemists and sales staff.

the new plant used natural fatty acids derived from coconut and palm kernel oils and from beef tallow. Increasing production from 5,000 to 20,000 ton tons per year was considered to be a bit of a gamble, but over the next few years it proved to be a very wise decision indeed. The plant was commissioned and handed over to the production department in November 1963.

During April 1965 a new continuous SO_3 sulphonation plant came on stream, which was capable of producing 14,000 tons of sulphated products per annum. In a statement to the press at the opening of the plant, on 26 April 1965, Frank Schon said:

We have specialised in the sulphation of fatty alcohols for many years and have been keen to replace the use of chlorosulphonic acid and oleum with SO_3 for some considerable time. We have operated a batch system for almost ten years and determined efforts to develop a continuous sulphonation plant started quite a long time ago. The present unit is the result of extensive research and development at pilot plant level. I am glad to say that the experience gained has allowed us to build a large plant using our own patented process. The plant is now on stream producing a range of alkyl and alkyl ether sulphates and alkyl benzene sulphonates of a much superior quality.

By the mid-1960s the old high-pressure unit was being used to hydrogenate lanolin (wool grease). The process hardened and whitened the lanolin which also lost its sheep dip odour, making it more acceptable to the cosmetics and pharmaceutical trades. The plant was also used to produce furfuryl alcohol from furfuraldehyde – a very exothermic reaction. After many months of safe operation by the development team and the provision of very clear operating instructions, the process was handed over to the production department. Unfortunately, they soon lost control of the process and the resultant explosion destroyed the plant, which was never rebuilt nor was the totally safe vapour phase hydrogenation process even considered by the shaken management.

By this time the Niro spray drier in S5 was completely inadequate for producing the tonnage of high active sodium lauryl sulphate required. An additional drier was needed. After many trials on the pilot facilities of several potential manufacturers, quotes were sought and the Scott Engineering Co. of Leven in Fyfe was chosen for the project. The whole installed cost for the drier, air heater and six-cyclone dust extraction system was £46,000. In the late 1990s it cost over half a million pounds just to replace the dust extraction system!

Two smaller plants were brought on steam in the early '60s, both of which made use of materials from other units within the factory for their feedstock.

The first was erected in 1961 for the manufacture of sulphamic acid from urea and SO_3. The product was sold under the A&W trade name of 'Amcide' – a total weed-killer which had the advantage of turning into a high nitrogen fertiliser a few weeks after use. The second plant was constructed in the old S2 building in 1964 to manufacture tertiary amines from sulphated lauryl alcohol. The amines were then converted into cationic surfactants in S1. These products, known as betaines, amine oxides and quaternaries, found use as baby shampoos, dishwasher liquids and bactericides for cooling towers and swimming pools and as sterilising agents for dairy equipment.

The company firmly believed that the welfare of its employees played an important part in the company's early success. The provision of a sports ground and pavilion within the factory site was just one example. Attending the opening of the new facilities were: Alex Lindsey (engineering director), Arthur Halfpenny (works director), Hans Abel (Solway site general manager), Otto Secher (sales director), Peter Baines (commercial director), Bob Dickie (technical director) and Frank Schon (chairman and managing director).

A shift manager adjusts the conditions on the monomer column during the first stage of the oil additive manufacturing process.

The monomer wash and feed vessels. A process operator adjusts the rate of flow of monomer into the feed vessel, prior to charging the polymerising vessel below.

Inorganics

Following concern about the availability of sulphuric acid for the production of detergent grade phosphates, it was proposed to increase production at Solway by the addition of a third kiln and acid plant. This project was expected to cost £850,000 and would increase production of both sulphuric acid and cement by 50,000 tons of each per annum. APCM would take the extra cement and, until further expansions on the phosphate plant took place, Solway would have 40,000 tons of sulphuric acid for sale on the open market at £10.5 per ton. In fact, by the end of November 1957 all external sales had ceased and all of the acid was used internally.

In May 1962, Lord Fleck, chairman of ICI Ltd, officially opened the third kiln and acid plant at Solway increasing the production of both cement and sulphuric acid by 70,000 tons per year. Despite this higher level of production, the internal demand for sulphuric acid was growing at such a rate that during the company's 25th birthday celebrations on 7 May 1965, Frank Schon announced yet another expansion would take place at Solway by the construction of two more kilns and acid lines. These would boost production by a further 160,000 tons of both cement and acid each year.

The main user of sulphuric acid was the phosphates plant and in December 1961 a third phosphoric acid plant (F3) was commissioned. The new plant was capable of producing 80,000 tons of P_2O_5 per annum and in June 1964 Edwin B. Lopker assigned two of his inventions and the whole of the benefit from them, in all countries in the world, to Marchon.

Sulphonation vessel No.11B in the newly constructed hydrotropes (Eltersol) plant where toluene, xylene or cumene were reacted with sulphuric acid. During the reaction water was stripped from the mixture to give the required product.

Opposite above: The Marchon Board of Directors presented medals to local councillors to commemorate their time as Mayor of the Borough of Whitehaven. The medals were to be worn at future council meetings, but the presentation of them led to the company being accused of buying favour from the council. Amongst the recipients were: Aldermen W. Stephenson, F. Harvey, T. Reed, F. Baxter, G. McCartney, W. Knipe, W. Pritchard, G. Hanlon, J. Blamire and J. Walsh.

Below: Peter Baines with M. Karim-Lamrani, the director general of OCP (The Office Cherifien des Phosphate of Morocco), after a meeting at Whitehaven to agree future requirements and prices for phosphate rock.

Management/finance

After several years close connection with Marchon–Solway, Sir Henry Tizzard was appointed to the board of directors of Solway chemicals on 22 March 1956.

On 22 March 1957 the Financial Times reported:

Albright March On
The Market took a favourable view of A&W results and marked the 5/- units up 9d to eighteen shillings and seven pence halfpenny. The dividend is being maintained at 18 per cent on the larger capital even though trading profits have risen from £3.76 million to £4.42 million. The comparative figure has been adjusted to take into account the acquisition of Marchon Products Ltd.

Clearly A&W Ltd shareholders were quick to reap the benefits of the merger and the *Birmingham Post* reported in March of the same year that:

Exports by Marchon Products Ltd, makers of sulphuric acid and detergent materials, who were recently taken over by A&W Ltd, are now twenty times greater than they were in 1950. They now account for 52.7 per cent of the total sales against only 14.3 in 1950. During the same period turnover has increased fivefold.

During April 1957 Fred Marzillier was appointed to the board of the Whitehaven Harbour Commissioners to look after the company's growing developments around the docks.

Bob Dickie, chief chemist and works general manager, was appointed to the board of directors of both Marchon Product and Solway Chemicals on 8 December 1958. At the same time, Otto Secher, sales director of Marchon, was made a director of Solway Chemicals.

Perhaps the most significant event of 1957 came on 19 November when the co-founder of the company – Fred Marzillier – resigned from his full-time executive directorships of both companies. He explained that his main reason for leaving the business he had worked so hard to establish, was that it had grown too big. He said 'When you no longer know 1,700 people by name, then you can no longer do them justice.' In a veiled reference to the takeover by A&W he added, 'It is the penalty of becoming part of a big organisation that all the creative satisfaction of running a concern that has grown from small beginnings is lost!'

Clearly Fred was very unhappy at having to seek the approbation of people in Birmingham for every scheme or change required at Whitehaven. Mr Marzillier was quickly replaced on the Marchon board by company secretary Peter Baines, who also stepped onto the boards of Solway Chemicals and the Astoria Shipping and Transport Co. Ltd, which had been set up to handle Marchon's transport needs.

For the conspicuous part that both Frank Schon and Fred Marzillier played in the economic redevelopment of Whitehaven they were elected freemen of the Borough of Whitehaven during 1961.

Following his election as a fellow of Kings College, Newcastle in November 1958, Frank Schon was further recognised when he was elected chairman of the Cumberland Development Council and also the North Regional Economic Planning Council which was based in Newcastle-upon-Tyne, during 1964.

By the end of 1965 Marchon Products Ltd were set up for yet more changes in management and organisation. These would have far-reaching effects.

Lord Fleck, the chairman of ICI Ltd, and Frank Schon deep in discussion at the official opening of Solway Chemicals third kiln and sulphuric acid plant.

Lord Fleck sees for himself what it's like inside the kiln at full load and heat input. The heat in the kiln was so intense that it could only be safely viewed through a welders mask.

Above: To commemorate the opening of the third kiln at Solway, a new road and roundabout were constructed on the site and named after Lord Fleck, who officially opened the plant.

Left: Number three sulphuric acid plant at Solway. The new plant increased the production of both sulphuric acid and cement to over 170,000 tons per annum.

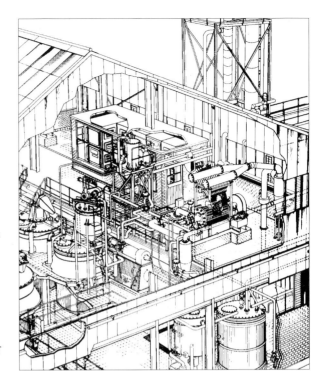

Right: The engineering layout diagram for the new SO$_3$ sulphonation plant, showing Marchon's patented Baker–Perkins reactor just to the right of centre.

Below: Joe McAllister, member of the sulphonation plant development and design team, checks on the progress of the construction of the new plant.

A general view of the new fatty alcohol plant in 1964 with the former NCB boiler house (dark coloured) on the right, which was used as the main inorganics pilot plant. It was here that the revolutionary purified phosphoric acid process was developed a few years later.

Three engineers from the main contractor, Lurgi GMBH of Frankfurt, alongside one of the electrolysers used to produce hydrogen and oxygen from caustic potash solution. The gases were produced at 30 atmospheres pressure (450lb per square inch).

Fred Marzillier and Frank Schon receive the Freedom of the Borough of Whitehaven from the mayor – Councillor Fred Baxter – in 1961.

Fatty alcohol plant shift manager and 'Russian hero' Bill Telford adjusting a feed/transfer pump on the new fatty alcohol plant. Before joining the fatty alcohol department Bill was a foreman in S1 building.

Prime Minister Harold Wilson chats to Marchon process workers and trade union convenors, Jimmy Jardine and John Walker, at Marchon's 25th birthday celebrations.

Trudy Schon and Mary Wilson in earnest discussion at the company's 25th anniversary party.

four

All Change
at the Top
1966–1975

Marchon received the Queen's Award to Industry for Export Achievement on three occasions during the period under review – 1966, 1969 and 1975 – recognising the growing strength of the company overseas. This degree of success required the involvement of Whitehaven-based sales managers together with a large team of overseas agents, and by 1968 the company was represented in eighty-eight countries across the globe.

Further recognition for the company came when Frank Schon was knighted in the Queen's Birthday Honours list of 1966.

Around the same time A&W Ltd engaged the American management consultants McKinsey to survey the whole of the group and make recommendations for improvements to the company's organisation and management structure. Their nine-month-long study led to a recommendation for major changes.

These changes called for wholly owned UK subsidiary companies to become operating divisions of the parent firm. A&W Ltd would be controlled by a chief executive with each operating division reporting directly to him. The direct supervision of staff functions, such as personnel, finance, research and development and patents, would move under the control of the chief executive in London. A&W Ltd directors would therefore only have one link with the manufacturing divisions – the new chief executive Edward R. Kinsley. The novel structure effectively centralised administration in Birmingham and London whilst moving the responsibility for running a profitable operation into the hands of the divisional managing directors.

On 19 April 1967, A&W announced the Belle Dune/A&W (Canada) fertiliser venture which was to cost C\$12 million; however, by June of the same year the capital required had grown to £15 million. New A&W Ltd chief executive Ed Kinsey stated 'The phosphorous kilns in Canada would produce 65,000 tons per year, growing to 100,000 tons over a five-year period and the Newfoundland venture would have no effect on Marchon.'

These events formed the background to Sir Frank Schon's letter of resignation from the board of A&W Ltd and from his position as chairman and managing director of all the Whitehaven companies, with effect from 5 May 1967.

In his letter to Sir Sydney Barratt, Frank Schon, chairman of A&W, wrote:

Dear Sydney,

There has been a history of disagreement on my part with Board policy. In the past I have recorded my differing views and left it at that. However the decision to move phosphorous manufacture from this country to Newfoundland, the general shift of emphasis in our operations from Europe to North America and the risks which are incumbent in these moves have further increased my concern as to the way in which the company is proceeding.

I have in the past expressed views about board reorganisation and specifically laid emphasis on the need to rejuvenate the board. I was willing to go along with the McKinsey reorganisation scheme but disagree with the way in which it is being put into effect and which, in my opinion, will have consequences highly unfavourable to the company.

I have been associated with Marchon since its inception 27 years ago. Over 2,000 people – and I feel very close to them – are now employed in what is considered to be a very successful part of the British chemical industry. For the past 11 years I have been associated with the A&W group and I believe I have made many friends throughout the organisation.

The Solway mine rescue team. From left to right: Bert Ratcliffe, Brian Fitzsimmons, Ted Holliday and Vince Hughes.

Marchon works executive team with A&W Ltd Chairman Sir Sydney Barrett. Standing, from left to right: Bert Harrington, George Pekarek, Bill Manning, Mike Cussons, Albert Taylor, Ernie Charlton, Bill Dawkins, Len Coulthard, Martin Rowe and John Hewitson. Front row, from left to right: Otto Secher, Adolf Koebner, Sir Sydney Barrett, Peter Baines, Arthur Halfpenny and Stan Kelly.

Peter Baines and Otto Secher receive Marchon's third Queen's Award to Industry for Export Achievement from the Lord Lieutenant of Cumbria, John Wade.

All this has made it difficult to reach my final decision which is to resign from the boards of A&W and its subsidiary companies; I do so with regret and would like my resignation to take effect from the earliest possible date.

Sir Sydney, who was deeply committed to the changes in management structure, had little option but to accept Schon's resignation, particularly in the light of Ed Kinsley's statement: 'Every effort has been made to devise an organisation into which Sir Frank Schon would fit, but there comes a time to draw the line if you are to achieve the management structure you want.' Clearly Frank Schon knew that there was no room in the new A&W Ltd structure for an entrepreneur such as himself.

Peter Baines, the administration director and company secretary, was appointed managing director of Marchon and Solway Chemicals with effect from 1 July 1967 and Otto Secher became chairman of the two companies at the same time.

These management manoeuvres left Peter Baines with the responsibility for the entire original Marchon group, and with all the boards of directors dissolved he noted 'In my task of divisional managing director I will be assisted by two groups of people who will report directly to me.' The first group was called the executive committee and the second were known as the controllers.

The changes in the company structure were completed in April 1968 when Marchon Products Ltd and Solway Chemicals Ltd became The Marchon Division; ACC Ltd became the ACC Division and A&W (mfg) Ltd became The Industrial Chemicals Division.

Otto Secher presents long service gold watches to Austin Sowerby, Stan Kelly and a female recipient. At Marchon, long service meant twenty-five years of unbroken service with the company.

Peter Baines was appointed to the board of directors of A&W Ltd in September 1970 and was replaced at Whitehaven by Otto Secher who remained as divisional managing director until he retired in March 1972. He was followed into the hot seat by Danny Fagandini. Otto Secher was deservedly honoured in the New Year's honours list of 1971 with a CBE for his services to exports.

The workforce at Whitehaven were stunned when, in a clumsy attempt to recoup some of the money going down the drain in Canada, 120 technical staff were made redundant with just one day's notice. All technical departments were badly affected with the research and the technical sales departments decimated. The remaining 650 members of staff quickly formed a branch of the trade union, ASTMS, and forced its recognition by the 21 December 1971. The rest of A&W followed suit six months later.

At the end of March 1971 A&W Ltd announced that Tenneco Inc. of Houston, Texas, had agreed to an unsecured loan of £17.5 million in return for an issue of 5 per cent convertible stock. This meant that A&W would pay Tenneco interest of 5 per cent on the loan without it being secured by any of their assets. The loan was finalised on 8 June 1971. A&W Ltd had also sold their very profitable business – Midlands Silicones – to the Dow Corporation of Midland, Michigan, for £3.5 million.

Faced with additional costs of £2,400 per day in interest charges alone, they decided to invest the whole of the Tenneco loan and the balance of the money from the Midland Silicones sale. A&W chairman Sir Richard Powell stated that '1971 was a better year for the A&W group than 1970 despite the troubles in Newfoundland. Profits were £2.9 million and all the UK divisions

Above left: Phosphate plant shift manager and process supervisor Billy Steel checks with process worker Harry Martin that everything is running smoothly.

Above right: The newly erected phosphoric acid concentrator on F3 acid plant in 1975. Process worker Alan Byers checks on progress.

showed improvements and we have derived some benefits from the investment of the Tenneco funds. These gains have been offset by increased losses in Newfoundland.

If ever proof was needed that Frank Schon knew what he was doing when he opposed the Canadian venture there it was straight from the chairman's mouth. Powell's statement also showed detergent materials sales of £29.6 million with a profit of £3.4 million.

In February A&W announced yet another change in the organisation of the company when the whole group was split into just two divisions: The Marchon Division and the Industrial Chemicals Division. This meant Whitehaven took on the added responsibility of ACC's fertiliser and farm protection business.

Inevitably, further management changes followed with A&W (Australia); Albright Moraji & Pandit (India); Polyphos (South Africa); A&W (Ireland) Ltd and all the European marketing agencies being added to Marchon's responsibilities. The Division was reorganised into profit accountable areas: Whitehaven, Europe, Agricultural and Australia, and John Wills succeeded Danny Fagandini as the Marchon Division managing director.

The profits of the Marchon division were reported to be substantially higher, despite increases in raw materials costs, particularly phosphate rock, which hit the division hard. Tenneco International Inc. exercised their option to convert £16.9 million of its loan to the company into 52 million units of ordinary stock and by the end of the year (1974) they held 58.554 million shares – 49.8 per cent of A&W Ltd.

Marchon's were awarded their third Queen's Award to Industry for Export Achievement in May 1975. The Division's exports had risen three-fold over the past three years and exceeded £25 million per annum. The award was presented at a ceremony on 16 June 1975 by John Wade, the Lord Lieutenant of Cumberland.

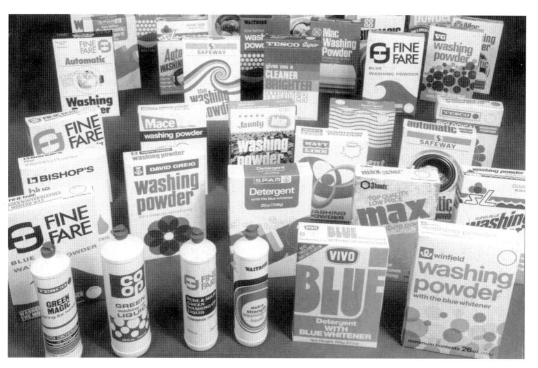

A selection of liquid and powder detergents manufactured and packed by Marchon for the supermarket trade.

The management merry-go-round continued when, on 5 December 1975, it was announced the Industrial Chemicals and the Marchon Divisions would be merged into one, to be called The Detergents and Chemicals Group, which in turn would be subdivided into six sectors. These were: Agriculture, Australia, Detergents, Organics, Phosphates and Specialities. Each sector would have its own executive committee reporting to John Wills, the managing director of the new group.

Inorganics

Kilns Nos 4 and 5 were commissioned at Solway on 7 January and 21 May 1967 respectively, boosting the production of cement and sulphuric acid by a further 160,000 tons per annum. At the time Solway was close to being the biggest manufacturer of sulphuric acid in the UK.

A new phosphoric acid plant – the fourth – which used the Kellogg Lopker process started production at a rate of 85,000 tons of P_2O_5 per annum in November 1968. The opening of the new plant allowed the first two acid plants at Whitehaven to close down. A second Bowen's spray drier was also commissioned which increased production of STPP. At the end of 1968 production of inorganic chemicals at Whitehaven had reached the following levels:

Sulphuric Acid: 350,000 tons per annum
Cement: 350,000 tons per annum
Phosphoric Acid: (P_2O_5)   165,000 tons per annum
STPP: 170,000 tons per annum

George W. Pekarek, A&W Ltd commercial general manager. Long serving George was also sales director of the Marchon Division.

In the late 1960s the rising cost of the production of sulphuric acid and cement from anhydrite became a serious cause for concern. With the market for cement falling rapidly, the anhydrite route labour intensive, and the heavy machinery involved needing constant and expensive maintenance, production costs escalated at an uncontrollable rate. These factors alone were sufficient to shift the economic balance in favour of progressively changing over to sulphur as the main raw material.

No.1 sulphur burner, which replaced kilns 1 and 2, was started up on 1 March 1973 with a capacity of 200,000 tons of sulphuric acid per year. No.3 kiln was replaced with a second burner on 28 November 1975, increasing capacity to 350,000 tons and just six months later the third sulphur burner came on stream raising sulphuric acid production to 525,000 tons per annum, making Solway the largest production site in the UK. The whole scheme cost £2.5 million but on the downside the change-over to sulphur burning reduced the Solway workforce by about 100 people. With Solway moving to sulphur burning a new sulphur terminal and storage facility was constructed at Workington dock which could handle up to 10,000-ton sulphur carriers.

An announcement was made on 12 December 1973 that £3.2 million would be invested on a new plant to produce 40,000 tons of purified phosphoric acid per year. The new process, known as the MO process, was developed jointly by Chemists from Oldbury and Marchon.

Organics

On 10 March 1975 the company announced it was to invest £1.35 million on a plant to produce imidaziline betaines which were used in the manufacture of very mild shampoos.

Above: Stencilling drums outside S6 stores before the new drumming off plant was built. Drums would come up to the stores from the manufacturing plants and were repainted and stencilled before they were sent to the customer.

Right: On his retirement, Fred Marzillier took the trouble to say his goodbyes to as many people as he could. Here he shakes hands with civil engineering manager Don Cooper.

Following page: A group of Marchon employees who collected their long-service awards in 1974. Amongst the recipients are: Hugh Fletcher, Ian Hepburn, Jim Smith, Arthur Moore, Bob Southward, Tom Cowling, David Williams, Alan Routledge, Pons Smith, Joe Tyson and Ken Wolstenholme, with Managing Director John R. Wills on the extreme right

Bob Armstrong, plant manager, logistics manager and internal transport manager. Bob had a long career at management level based around the detergents plants.

The Barton-on-Humber agricultural chemicals complex which was managed by Marchon for a number of years. This was the first plant in the world to make compound fertilisers by the prilling process. Phosphoric acid from Marchon was delivered by ship to the company's own jetty on the Humber estuary.

Part of Marchon's new blending plant for agricultural chemicals at Barton. A new charge of raw materials is being pumped to the plant from the outside storage tanks.

A general view of Marchon's updated detergent powder packing lines in S4 building. The operator is loading flat packets to the machine, which squares and glues them before filling and final sealing.

Above: It takes several different engineering skills to get a project from design to the finished plant. From left to right: Ian Hartley (project engineer), Joe McAllister (chemical engineer), George McMillan (engineering drawing) and Ian Hepburn (project engineer).

Left: Bert Harrington, personnel and welfare director. Bert had a very good understanding with the trade unions and the workforce in general and always had their welfare at heart.

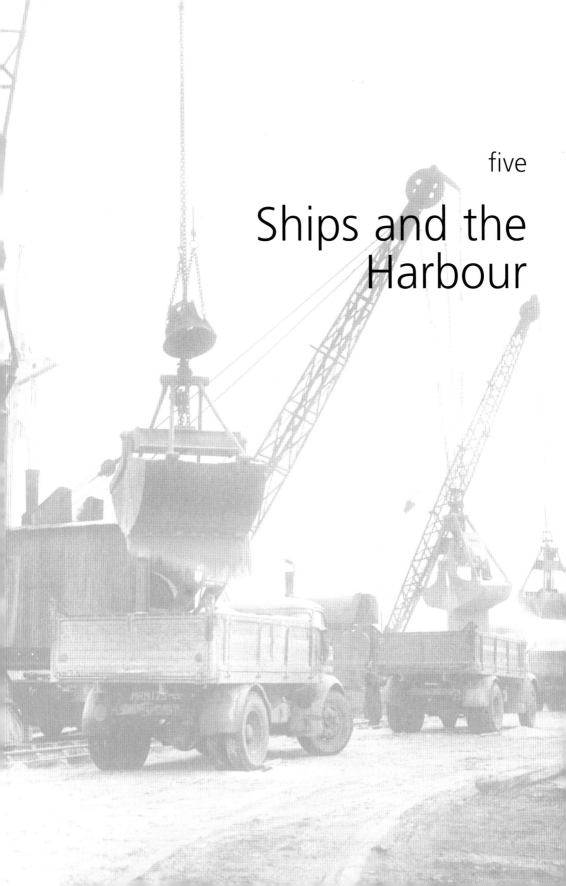

five

Ships and the Harbour

Left: Loading detergent powder into a Polish vessel for shipment to eastern Europe. Overseeing the job is John Eilbeck, Marchon's earliest employee.

Opposite: Otto Secher and Fred Marzillier look absolutely delighted as they watch the first load of detergent being loaded on board ship at Whitehaven's Queens Dock in 1950.

When a company as big as Marchon is located hundreds of miles away from its customers and the source of its raw material supplies, transport becomes a problem. Once large-scale production became the norm the company had to take a serious look at all forms of transport. In the 1940s most materials travelled by rail and later road transport bore the brunt; however, once the need for phosphate rock arose, then the sea was the only logical method of shifting hundreds of thousands of tons from Morocco to Whitehaven.

Whitehaven harbour is tidal and, at the time, had one wet dock capable of accommodating ships of up to 2,400 tons. Moreover, all ships using the harbour had to meet the limits of dimensions placed upon them by the dock gate width and the depth of water at the dock sill. The vessels had to be capable of making the return run to Morocco on a regular basis and the hiring of suitable vessels was not the easiest of tasks but Marchon were fortunate in having a good shipping agent – James Fisher & Sons of Barrow-in-Furness – to do this for them.

The ships

To get round the problems the company decided to have their own vessels built to very exacting specifications. The first of these ships – the *Marchon Trader* – was built by Austin & Pickersgill of Sunderland and was launched in the traditional way by Gertrude, the wife of Frank Schon, on 28 May 1957. The vessel cost £249,924 and had a dead weight of 2,500 tons, a 40ft 6ins beam, was 265ft in length and could carry a crew of up to twenty-one.

A second vessel – the *Marchon Enterprise* – followed, this time built by Clelland & Co. at their Wallsend yards on the Tyne. The 2,400-ton *Enterprise* was a touch shorter than the *Trader* at 241ft, with a breadth of 38ft 10in and a draught of 16ft 10in. The ship was launched by Marjory Secher on 9 November 1961, when her new captain received the following cable from the *Trader:*

The day has come old Trader *sings*
when young Enterprise *spreads his wings,*
Come on son, now don't delay
you'll soon be known throughout the bay.
To you your cargo may come as a shock
but we're quite sure its phosphate rock.

When the ship was launched, a third vessel was already on the stocks, identical to the *Enterprise,* the *Marchon Venturer* was launched in February 1962.

The vessels were able to keep up with Marchon's demands for phosphate rock for a few years but by 1965 a new method of delivery was needed which would involve the use of bulk carriers, transferring their cargoes at sea off Whitehaven.

The harbour

During March 1964 Marchon agreed a lease with the Whitehaven Harbour Commissioners for 'the demise to the company part of the quay of the Queens Dock and the dock quay with rights to erect specified works and railway tracks and the prior right to berth vessels for a period of ninety-nine years beginning on 1 October 1963 at an exclusive rent of £150 per annum.'

The first development to be completed at the harbour was the erection of two large silos and a conveyor system for the storage of phosphate rock. The installation was open by Sir Fergus Graham, Lord Lieutenant of Cumberland, on 2 July 1963.

The cartons of detergent packets were loaded using makeshift chutes with the whole operation a distinctly dry weather activity.

Prior to this, ships carrying rock were unloaded at the docks by grabs into bunkers which were used to fill a fleet of fifteen or more 8-ton lorries. These transported the material to the works, at Kells, via the town centre. The system had a number of drawbacks, not least of which was the spillage of the sand-like phosphate rock around the town, much to the annoyance of local residents and tradespeople. The system was slow and dirty, often leading to delays in the turn round of the ships.

The need to speed up turnaround times was paramount if the company was to receive all of the raw material it wanted. The use of the silos and new electrically operated cranes allowed the unloading of up to 359 tons of rock per hour and a vessel could be turned round on a single tide. The silos, which were built by John Laing & Sons, stood 96ft tall, had walls 6in thick and stood on a raft of concrete supported on 200 piles driven into the bedrock. The conveyor system ran round three sides of the dock.

Ensuring fast and efficient movement from the dock to the factory were a number of purpose-built 16-ton AEC Mammoth lorries, able to avoid spillage and to be loaded by gravity from the silos. Each lorry cost £5,000 and could be loaded in two to three minutes and, when in use sixteen hours a day, each vehicle could move 325 tons of rock to the factory on a two-shift basis.

By 1965 Marchon required 300,000 tons of rock per annum with the figure likely to rise to well over half a million tons. In practice Marchon's three vessels could handle 50,000 tons each in a year, half of what was needed. Faced with this situation there was little alternative other than to bring loads of up to 30,000 tons by bulk carrier to Whitehaven and to transfer the rock into the smaller vessels which could unload in the harbour. Bulk carriers of 26,000 tons capacity were chartered from the Norwegian consortium, AS Bulkhandling, and unloaded, at sea, into the

Watched by her husband Frank, Trudy Schon launches Marchon's first custom-built ship, the *Marchon Trader* at Austin & Pickergill's Sunderland ship yards, in May 1957.

The *Marchon Trader* slips into the river Weir watched by the men who built her.

Marchon vessels and a new, purpose-built barge – *Odin*. This method of discharge quickly settled into a smooth operation with only inclement weather causing any interruption. In that event the carriers moved across the Solway Firth to the sheltered waters on the Scottish side and unloading continued without further trouble. A 26,000-ton load of rock represented several weeks supply for the factory and its storage and movement took careful planning to ensure costly double handling was kept to a minimum. During normal unloading part of the rock was moved directly to the user plants and some was stored in blister hangers at the factory; the remainder was held in the silos and in the transfer vessels.

Bulk traffic controller at the dock, Des Haig, was instrumental in ensuring that there were no problems and that rock was always available when required.

In view of the importance of the movement of materials by sea, not only to Marchon but also to other industries in the county, Frank Schon suggested to Cumberland County Council in 1964 that they should carry out a survey into potential harbour requirements and come up with a plan to meet industry's needs. For one reason or another, the county council did nothing and it was left to Marchon to commission expert opinion from Sir Bruce White, Wolf, Barry and partners. By 1966 it became clear that there were three possibilities:

1 Do nothing
2 Build a new off-shore port near the factory which would only benefit Marchon with the
   resultant loss of trade, likely to be difficult for the Harbour Commissioners to swallow
3 Carry out major improvements to Whitehaven harbour

Marchon's second vessel – the *Marchon Enterprise* – under tow after being launched by Mrs Margery Secher, at the Clelland yards on the river Tyne, on 9 November 1961.

The latter proposal was selected and a full study of the existing harbour was carried out by sinking a series of bore-holes into the sea bed, and by making many hydrographical measurements. The effects of wind and tide were studied by constructing a very large scale model of the harbour and its approaches, and subjecting it to tests by wind and wave generating machines. As a result of these investigations, it was proposed to build a deep water harbour within the Customs House Dock, capable of taking 30,000-ton vessels. Access was to have been provided by a deeply dredged channel one mile long and the outer harbour would also have been dug out to allow the big ships to turn around.

The final scheme would have cost £3 million and when Marchon presented it to the commissioners and the various local councils and industries, they had already spent several hundred thousand pounds on the survey alone. Hopes of any financial input from outside sources quickly faded despite a guarantee of £200,000 per year from Marchon in the form of landing fees. Once again the reticence of local people to invest their money led to the scheme being dropped. In the end the only way forward was to stand still; bulk deliveries of phosphate rock continued until 1992, when the last bulk carrier – *Havkatt* – left after discharging 27,000 tons of Moroccan rock.

After nearly twenty years' service at Whitehaven the *Marchon Venturer* was sold to the Annan Shipping Co. During its stay, the *Venturer* made about 275 round trips to Casablanca. Instead of phosphate rock, the vessel would transport coal and scrap iron under the flag of its new owner, who renamed the ship the *Chon Vent*.

Thus, after almost fifty years of close connection with Whitehaven harbour Marchon never used the facilities again and cleared the site after dismantling the conveyor belts and demolishing the silos. For just about the first time in its history Whitehaven harbour was devoid of all regular commercial shipping.

The *Marchon Venturer*, built by Clelland, steams out of Whitehaven harbour en route to Casablanca for a load of phosphate rock.

The barge *Odin* was specially built in Norway for ferrying phosphate rock from the bulk carriers to the harbour at Whitehaven. The vessel was owned and operated by James Fisher & Sons of Barrow-in-Furness.

The phosphate rock silos and conveyor system under construction at the Queens Dock, Whitehaven, viewed looking back from the bulwark in 1963.

The completed system ran round three sides of the dock. The system comprises two 3,000-ton silos, the conveyors and a small fleet of purpose-built lorries and cost a total of £150,000.

The *Odin* being unloaded at Whitehaven in 1976.

The harbour installation was opened by Sir Fergus Graham, Lord Lieutenant of Cumberland, seen here on the extreme left talking to Frank Schon, John Walker (craftsmen's union convenor), Jimmy Jardine (GMB Union branch secretary) and director Arthur Halfpenny.

A rock lorry demonstrates the loading technique to an audience of guests at the official opening of the installation.

A lorry driver sends a signal from a transmitter on the roof of the cab to a receiver on the silo. The signal then actuated an outlet valve on the silo and discharged 16 tons of phosphate rock from the silo into the specially built lorry.

From the offloading point within the factory the rock was transported by a series of conveyors to the storage silos on the phosphoric acid plant. Note the old Ladysmith Pit coal washeries in the background.

A rock lorry tipping phosphate rock at the plant. The lorries were designed to prevent any spillage of their load on its journey through the town to the works.

The harbour pilot boat leaves the barge *Odin* being loaded up with phosphate rock from the bulk carrier *Bangor*.

Some of the many Cumbrian businessmen who attended the open day at the hydrology labs in London where the model of the harbour was under test. They are clustered round the existing south harbour area.

The large scale model of Whitehaven harbour used to assess the effects of wind and tide on the harbour. The proposed modifications would have allowed the handling of 30,000-ton vessels within the confines of the south harbour.

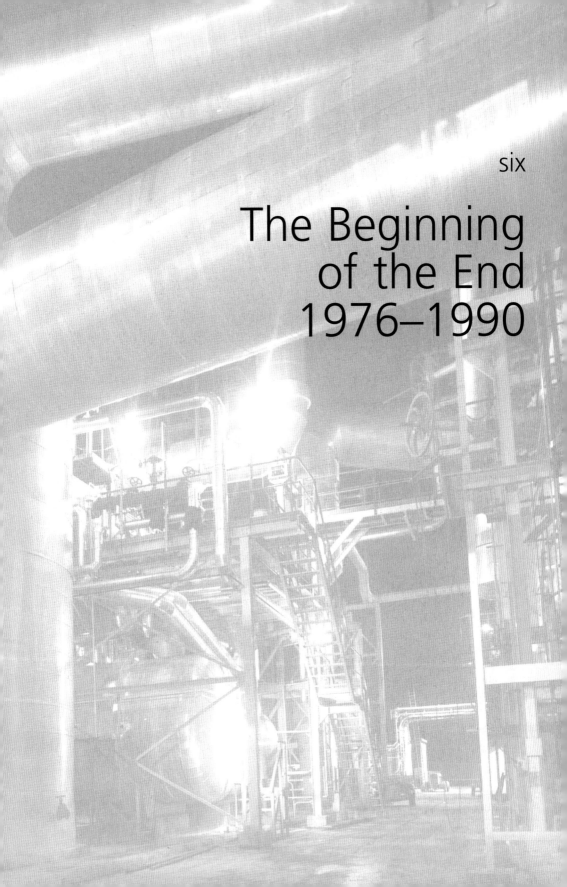

six

The Beginning of the End 1976–1990

Management

A vital part of the new Detergents and Chemicals Group was its sales department, staffed by people drawn from the former divisions of the company. The department's first manager, appointed in 1976, was Bill Adair who was also responsible for the worldwide phosphates business. Ian Black was appointed chief accountant at the same time but remained based in Whitehaven. Danny Fagandini was put in charge of 'special assignments' reporting directly to A&W's managing director, David Livingstone. Amongst his tasks Danny studied areas for collaboration with Tenneco.

Key figures in the company report for 1976 made interesting reading, including the statement that the average wage for A&W workers had reached £3,800 per annum. Productivity, measured in sales per employee was £25,000 per annum and at the time the Whitehaven site employed 2,188 people.

Despite the fact that Canadian phosphorus production was still in deep trouble, the company planned to sink much more money abroad, particularly in the Americas. By the end of 1976 the management of the Detergents & Chemicals Group had been more or less finalised with several Whitehaven-based people holding senior posts, including: Mike Cussons, director of engineering; George Pekarek, commercial director; Martin Rowe, works director; Albert Taylor, technical director; David Wigham, chief buyer, and John Wills managing director.

Danny Fagandini was given yet another job in 1977 when he was made the general manager of central development, where he looked at the long term strategic development of the company at home and overseas.

The principal event of 1977 at Whitehaven was the retirement of transport manager and director of the Astoria Shipping and Transport Co., Stan Kelly. After completing thirty-one years with the company, Stan was justifiably proud of the fact the company never lost a customer because his goods had arrived late, and in the lifetime of the transport department there had never been a legal summons or serious injury arising out of an accident involving a Whitehaven driver.

After just eighteen months of operation, the Detergents & Chemicals Group was disbanded and the group managing director, John Wills, was made a main board director. Martin Rowe then took over responsibility for the whole of the Whitehaven Works with effect from June 1979. The Albright World noted 'these appointments are part of changes in our organisation designed to strengthen and simplify our company structure to give further responsibility to the six business sectors set up eighteen months ago.' John Wills added 'no redundancies and very few transfers to other locations are involved.' At the same time it was announced A&W sales had reached £1 million per day.

The long-awaited Marchon Sports and Social Club was erected at Corkickle in 1977 and was opened by John Wade, the Lord Lieutenant of Cumberland. The building cost £185,000 and had a full membership of 1,900. The building was paid for by the company but run by the members.

The company's American owners, Tenneco International, decided to visit all their European locations in 1980, including Whitehaven. The visiting party included Tenneco president, Jack Diesel, executive vice-presidents, George Mason, Stan Allison and Ken Reece, and chairman and chief executive Jim Ketelson. They flew into Carlisle airport in the company jet and were chauffeured down to Whitehaven where they were met by David Livingstone and the other main board directors. Ketelson said the main reason for the visit was to review the progress of the 'Tenneco-isation' of the company and to set the next five-year plan!

Marchon chauffeurs George Hailes, Max Wilson and George Smith standing by their cars, in front of the company aircraft, waiting for the visitors from Tenneco Inc. at Carlisle Airport.

Marchon works executive committee, *c*.1980. From left to right: Raymond Gallagher (general manager personnel), Ken Wolstenholme (works chemist), Martin Rowe (Whitehaven works director), Terry Palmer (works manager) and Len Coulthard (chief engineer).

Local MP Dr Jack Cunningham was a regular visitor the Marchon works. Seen here in discussion with Martin Rowe and Len Coulthard, Dr Cunningham was an advisor and consultant to the whole of the A&W Ltd Group.

A conference was held in 1982, to allow the workers' representatives to express their views on the way the company was being run. The staff, in particular, were concerned about the level of overseas investment and Marchon staff union officer, Richard Stables said 'investment by the company per UK employee is too low and this is the reason for low productivity. It is not that the UK workforce is less able or lazier. Selling our skills abroad is fine, but we should not be putting most of our investment capital overseas.' A&W chairman David Livingstone replied 'Although UK wages are lower; overall wages costs are higher because our UK workers really do produce less. We have no option but to invest abroad if we are to stay in business and anyone who does not think the situation is that bad in A&W in the UK does not understand the problem.'

Two major projects for the Whitehaven site were announced in late 1989, the first of which was for £2.8 million to replace the factory's boiler house. The second, costing £1.7 million, was for the refurbishment of No.1 sulphuric acid plant. Group general manager, Ian Black said 'These projects reflect the confidence of both the Tenneco and A&W boards in the long term future of the Whitehaven factory.'

During a visit to the factory by local councillors, works director Terry Palmer told them, 'The profit performance is still short of our target but we are moving closer.' Environmental manager

Alan Shepherd said 'My appointment reflects the company's belief that good environmental management at Whitehaven has top priority.'

Major changes in working practice at the Whitehaven works were agreed and signed by management and unions during 1989. This flexibility deal was designed to end job demarcation and restrictive practices within the works and to get the deal through the company had to make a significant one off lump sum payment and additional pay increases over the next three years. Instead of narrowly defining a craftsman's work, 'the enabling agreement', to give it its proper name, set out the general principles which governed the execution of all craft work on the site. 'Hereafter craftsmen will carry out any task required, subject to them having the necessary skills and sufficient time and that all safety aspects were met.' Two hundred and thirty craftsmen attended a fourteen-week training course to ensure that they did have the necessary skills. Planning manager Terry Ponting noted 'There is less cost and greater satisfaction in seeing a job through from start to finish.'

During August 1989 the company were asked by the local media to clarify their position on certain environmental problems and on the future of Marchon. Asked about emissions in general the company replied 'A number of accidental emissions had occurred over the past eighteen months and these were as unacceptable to Marchon as anyone else.'

Marchon works full executive committee in 1982. From left to right: -?-, George Pekarek, Ian Black, Martin Rowe, Brian Milling, Bert Harrington and David Wigham.

General view of the phosphates area, looking south, with the inorganics pilot plant in the left foreground and the new (F5) phosphoric acid plant under construction.

Discharges into the Irish Sea were being tackled and the company was spending a great deal of money dealing with the unsightly slick of foam on the surface of the sea. More important was the discharge of gypsum from the phosphoric acid plant. The effluent contains some heavy metals, which come into the plant as impurities in the phosphate rock, including: cadmium, zinc, lead, arsenic and uranium. The treatment of these metals was ongoing and always met allowable limits.

There was a suggestion that Marchon had no long term future, a fact the company denied. Although A&W refused to sanction the spending of £6.0 million for the refurbishment of part of the sulphuric acid plant, they had sanctioned £2.8 million for a new boiler house.

Whitehaven got a new works director when John Markham replaced Terry Palmer with effect from 6 November 1989. Terry was transferred to A&W's European headquarters at Warley to look after special projects.

During an address at the long service celebrations of 1990, works director John Markham stated 'there is a bright future ahead for us. If we make the improvements I have in mind, we will get the support we need to refurbish the older plants and to build new plants.' Fine sentiments! Unfortunately they were not fulfilled.

F5 phosphoric acid plant viewed at night. This was the last phosphate plant at the factory to manufacture the acid from phosphate rock and sulphuric acid. In the end it proved to have a relatively short life!

Organics

The manufacture of sulphamic acid ceased at Whitehaven at the beginning of January 1976 after A&W agreed to a deal with the Japanese company – Nissan Chemical Industries. At the time Nissan were the world's largest producers of the material and A&W became their sole European agent.

The new amine plant was commissioned in February 1977. Costing £1.35 million the new plant offered a greatly increased production capacity for the amines and their derivatives.

A&W announced a £3.0 million expansion to the oil additives plant and works manager Terry Palmer said 'the new development reflects A&W's announced intention to develop and strengthen the Whitehaven Works, the company's largest site and the confidence of Tenneco in the long term future here.' The expansion work was completed and commissioned by the New Year of 1990. The level of success of the oil additives business was such that the plant merited its own business unit headed by Paul Smith with Jim Archibold managing the sales function. Both men were based at Warley, some 200 miles away from the plant!

During 1982 the works engineering department commissioned a purpose-built control and management system for the powder detergent packing lines. Microchips ensured the packets were filled accurately and provided information needed by management and the statutory bodies.

The fabric conditioner plant was constructed on the site of the old organics pilot plant behind S1 building, overlooking the Solway Firth.

A new precipitator was installed at the SO$_3$ sulphonation plant during 1988 to prevent further emissions of acid foam. It became necessary following a number of incidents when the paintwork on employees' cars was damaged. The problem was caused when tail gases from the sulphonation plant were vented into the Solway chimney. Here they mixed with acid mist to form an acid foam which carried some distance from the top of the 450ft chimney. The new 25,000 volt electrostatic precipitator eliminated the problem. Later A&W announced an investment of £2.6 million to increase SO$_3$ sulphonation capacity at Whitehaven, particularly of fatty alcohols and their derivatives. The new plant came on stream during 1991.

Inorganics

A new phosphoric acid concentrator, capable of producing 60,000 tons of concentrated phosphoric acid per year was commissioned during the spring of 1976, providing an important element in the phosphate complex. The capacity of the new phosphoric acid plant (F5) was almost 250,000 tons per year. With the new MMO purified wet acid plant also on stream, Marchon were then able to manufacture 130,000 tons of pure phosphoric acid per annum. The MMO plant was opened by HM the Queen Elizabeth II in March 1980. Both pure acid plants were further modified and enlarged, first in 1984 and again in 1987. These changes allowed the plants to produce more than a quarter of a million tons of technical and food grade phosphoric acid – a technical capability and flexibility that no other manufacturer in the world could better.

A solvent distillation column
on the fabric conditioner plant.
The view from its platform on a
good day was spectacular.

During the late 1980s the demolition of the Solway kilns started in real earnest and
engineer George Burns said 'we are tackling the biggest programme of demolition ever seen at
Whitehaven.' Modern chemical plants are amongst the most expensive things anyone can build
– it's more expensive for a given area than a modern hospital, luxury hotel or block of flats yet,
in a few years, when its economic life is over, there is nothing more worthless. There is nothing
more distressing for a worker than to look at a derelict site where he once worked. A&W started
the removal of the redundant plant in 1988 and the demolition work still continues today.

Sulphur burners replaced the anhydrite/cement kilns as the source of sulphur dioxide for the acid process during the early 1970s.

A sulphur burner viewed from the opposite side. The burner itself is the horizontal vessel at the bottom of the photograph.

No 1 & 2 ACID PLANTS SOLWAY AFTER CONVERTING TO SULPHUR BURNER

Diagram labels: 50°C; DILUTION AIR; TO HUMIDIFIERS & PRECIPITATORS; 70°C; AIR FROM ATMOSPHERE; 440°C 10.35% SO2; 70°C 70°C; 15; 1; 2; 3; 7; 8; 10; 11; 12; 30°C; 18; 21; 13; 14; 4; 5 1100°C; 6 475°C; 432°C; 9; 17; 16; 19; 20; FROM No 2 STREAM DRYING TOWERS; 50°C; 200°C; 70°C

1,2 & 3 DRYING TOWERS (EXISTING)
4 MAIN BLOWER (NEW)
5 SULPHUR BURNER (NEW)
6 PRIMARY WASTE HEAT BOILER (NEW)
7 CONVERTOR (EXISTING)
8 SECONDARY WASTE HEAT BOILER (NEW)
9 ECONOMISER (NEW)
10 OLEUM TOWERS (EXISTING)
11 & 12 ABSORBTION TOWERS (EXISTING)

13 DRYING TOWER & CIRCULATION TANK (EXISTING)
14 DRYING TOWER & CIRCULATION PUMPS (EXISTING)
15 DRYING TOWER & COOLERS (EXISTING)
16 OLEUM TOWER CIRCULATION TANK (EXISTING)
17 OLEUM TOWER CIRCULATION PUMP
18 OLEUM TOWER COOLERS (NEW)
19 ABSORBTION TOWER CIRCULATION TANK (EXIST)
20 ABSORBTION TOWER CIRCULATION PUMPS (NEW)
21 ABSORBTION TOWER COOLERS (EXISTING)

Opposite above: Schematic diagram of Nos 1 and 2 sulphur burners and sulphuric acid plants at Solway after conversion from the anhydrite process.

Opposite below: Unloading a tanker of molten sulphur, which had been brought to the works from the sulphur handling facilities at Workington Docks which could handle 10,000 ton vessels.

Right: An automated drum filling head on the new drumming and blending plant. The system ensured automatic filling of the drum, to the correct weight every time. The system ensured spillage (and therefore loss of profit) was cut to a minimum.

Below: General view of the new blending and drumming facilities in April 1984.

Marchon workers waiting in the snow to cheer the arrival of HM Queen Elizabeth II, in March 1980. She carried out the official opening of the MO plants.

The Queen, accompanied by A&W Ltd managing director David Livingstone, meets members of the Marchon workforce, their wives and members of local government at the Marchon works in March 1980.

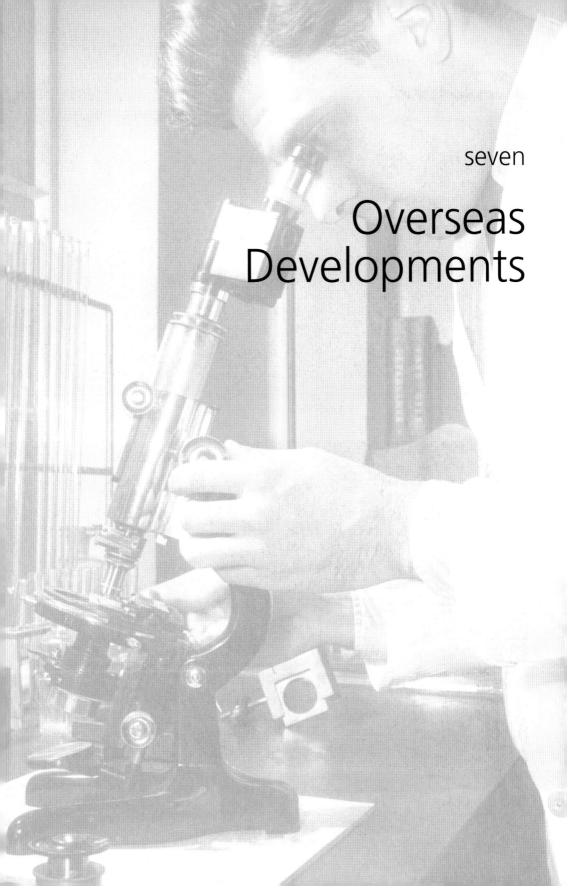

seven

Overseas
Developments

Italy

In anticipation of the UK joining the Common Market, Marchon formed their first overseas subsidiary Marchon Italiana SPA on 20 November 1958, with Danny Fagandini as its first managing director. It was not, however, until 20 March 1961 that production of a limited range of detergents and toiletry materials started at the new factory in Castiglione delle Stiviere. All was not smooth sailing and there were difficulties between Danny Fagandini and the Italian advisor, Mr Mancini, who was told by Frank Schon that the project would only go ahead if Danny Fagandini was in sole charge for a minimum of three years. Schon got his way!

The Albright World, the company's in-house magazine, announced in the December 1965 issue that:

A plant for the manufacture of A&W's Phosbrite chemical polishing solutions was opened alongside Marchon Italiana's factory at Castiglione delle Stiviere on 9 September. The solutions which are marketed in Italy under the trade name – Albrite – are used for polishing aluminium and brass. The new plant shares Marchon Italiana's factory and services but belongs to another Marchon subsidiary company – Cambria Spa – which was set up earlier in the year to manufacture and market A&W (mfg)'s chemical polishing solutions.

In 1972 Marchon Italiana received the coveted European award – Mercurio d'Oro – from Camillo Ripamonti, the Minister of Foreign Trade, at a ceremony in Rome on 13 May in the

The first manufacturing plant to be built overseas and to carry Marchon in its name was Marchon Italiana located at Castiglione-del-Stivere. The plant was erected in 1958 and has grown enormously since then.

One of the later Italian manufacturing units was built on three floors, each of which was open to the atmosphere. The whole structure was erected on large steel wheels and pulled into place for final piping up.

presence of the Italian Prime Minister, Giulio Andriotti. The award was made annually by the Centro Giornalistico Anzali and was the only recognition of its kind then existing in Italy for the contribution of industries to the economic development of Italy.

During the same year, the second Marchon plant in Italy – Marchon Sud – came on stream. Located at Frosinone, some 85km south of Rome, it was built to be nearer the customer base for detergent ethoxylates. Between 1974 and 1979 managing director, Giorgio Mira, expected A&W to spend another £3 million in Italy on further expansion. The bottle blowing plant at Marchon Sud started production in July 1976 and within six months seven highly automated bottle blowing lines were working twenty-four hours a day producing between 400 and 1,000 bottles each per hour depending on size and weight. The bottle filling unit could fill, label and box up to 4,000 bottles per hour. By 1977 the Frosinone site covered 190,000 square metres and employed well over 100 people.

The new microbiology laboratory, set up at Castiglione in 1977, under the management of Giuliano Mazzola, carried out biological examinations on all liquid detergents, cosmetic and toiletry formulations to ensure all Marchon Italiana's products met government regulations. At the same time A&W's new chromium plating process – Alecra 3 – was being piloted at Castiglione and joined their other metal treatment processes.

Frosinone was expanded again when a £3 million sulphonation and sulphation plant was started up in the spring of 1980. The development was overseen by Whitehaven project engineer John Hennedy, who worked closely with Marchon Italiana's consultant engineer Feruccio Lattanzi.

Dishwashing liquid detergents were packed at both Marchon Italiana locations using state of the art equipment. The manufacture of packing machinery of every kind has been a strong point of Italian industry for many years; indeed, the powder packing lines at Whitehaven were of Italian origin.

France

The company further strengthened its position in Europe when it set up a second subsidiary plant at St Mihiel, north of Paris, on 11 June 1968. The plant, which cost £500,000 to erect, came on stream in December 1969. In August 1976, A&W Ltd announced that they were to invest £2.4 million in expanding the production of detergent materials in France. The project went ahead despite the tragic death of the managing director Mike Dufaye, who was killed on his way home from the airport. Roy Harrison took over as managing director in his place. Since the plant started, Marchon France had grown quickly and by the end of 1977 was producing the whole range of Marchon's products.

A&W Ltd announced that under a co-operation agreement with BP Chemicals, they were to build a large ethoxylation plant at BP's French refinery at Lavera. Close to Marseilles, Lavera was ideally situated for the supply of Marchon's customers in Europe. Ethylene oxide was transferred, by pipeline, direct from the BP works. When this new facility started to produce, the Whitehaven plant would close down. The project was approved in December 1989 and commissioned during August 1991. With a capacity of 70,000 tons per year, the ethoxylation unit was the biggest in Europe.

The original glass-lined sulphonation vessels at Castiglione were multi-purpose and could be used for several products.

Spain

The plan to build Marchon's fourth European factory, at Alcover in Spain, was announced on 12 July 1970. Marchon Espanola started production in November 1972. In justifying the new plant, when the company already had two factories in Italy, one in France and headquarters in Whitehaven, Marchon Espanola's administration director Mike Fearfield said 'with import duties running between 30 and 50 per cent, the only way to expand our sales in Spain is through local manufacture.'

Marchon Espanola was the direct responsibility of Marchon Italiana, who had invested £350,000 in the venture. Managing director Giorgio Mira said 'with supplies coming from only a few miles away, the customer can not only call for technical advice and service more quickly, but he can carry smaller stocks and expect quick delivery at short notice.'

Marchon acquired the Spanish company, Surfac, in 1985 and a number of investments were made in the new company – Marchon Surfac – to expand capacity and update equipment. Marchon Surfac won the A&W safety award, the Martin Rowe Trophy, for the first time in 1989.

David Williams, Marchon Italiana's commercial manager in the company's early days, at Castiglione. David started with Marchon as a shift chemist on the detergents plant in 1949. He transferred to the commercial side working under Otto Secher before moving to Italy.

Asia

Marchon turned their sights towards Indonesia in the late 1970s, selling Whitehaven-produced materials through their agents, Commercial Supplies Ltd. Visits by Marchon sales staff in 1968, '69, '70 and '73 led to a rapid rise in demand. Shortly afterwards Marchon had manufacturing facilities in Malaysia, Singapore and the Philippines.

It was announced in 1977 that A&W had acquired, for cash, the share capital of Josen Chemical, a Malaysian company. The deal, which cost 3 million Malay dollars (£700,000), was approved by the government on the basis that Malayan participation would commence in 1980 and by 1990 they would hold 49 per cent of the company. Based in Kelang, Josen were the only phosphoric acid producers from thermal phosphorus in South East Asia. In 1980 the production of thermal acid was doubled. The acid was used for palm oil refining, sugar refining and in the production of natural rubber.

A&W acquired a 45 per cent share holding in UIC Organics Pty of Singapore, a subsidiary of the United Industrial Corporation Ltd. UIC was formed in 1977 to operate a new 7,000 ton per year sulphonation plant and when the deal was finalised it became known as Marchon–UIC (Pty) Ltd, a name which reflected the worldwide trade respect for the Marchon name. Whitehaven-based chemical engineer Joe McAllister and chemist Jimmy McDonald spent a year steering the project through.

South Africa

Eric Hudson, Marchon's technical relations officer (environment), was appointed commercial manager of Marchon Paragon Holdings (Pty) Ltd in South Africa. The company had been set

John Hewitson and wife Mary with their daughter, after John had picked up his honour from Buckingham Palace. John was Marchon Italiana's first works accountant and later became managing director of A&W (Ireland) Ltd.

up as a joint venture in 1976 to manufacture and market detergent and toiletries intermediates. During 1980 Marchon Paragon merged with AKULU Chemicals (Pty). AKULU was a joint venture formed in 1970 between AKZO Chemie in Holland and Chemical Holdings (Pty) in South Africa. The company then employed eighty-eight people and had a turnover of 7 million Rand (£3.8 million).

A&W Ltd announced its intention of divesting some of its overseas interests when the company sold its shares in two South African companies – SA Paper Chemicals Ltd and AKULU–Marchon – to Chemical Services Ltd. A&W Ltd had decided to take the offer from Chemical Services Ltd because the rate of inflation was high in South Africa at the time and the value of the Rand had fallen significantly.

America

During 1987 *The Albright World* reported on developments at Lee Creek in the USA:

The purified wet acid plant being built as a joint venture between A&W, Texasgulf and the Olin Corporation will be the largest and most modern plant of its kind in the USA. The technology derives from Marchon and was developed at Whitehaven. Whitehaven personnel involved at Lee Creek are Tom Sowerby (the project engineer), John McGeehan, Mark Rose and Alan Williams.

Lee Creek, works manager, plus five of his foremen, a process engineer and four process operators visited Whitehaven to study the process. The plant had a production rate of 120,000 tons per annum and was officially opened by James G. Martin, the governor of North Carolina, on 5 March 1990.

The spinning disc, co-current, spray drier newly installed at Castiglione, gave the company much needed flexibility in producing high active fatty alcohol sulphate for toothpastes and pharmaceutical products. Up to that point, Marchon Italiana bought in their requirements from Whitehaven.

Dr Giulieno Bossini, commercial director of Marchon Italiana and later the whole of A&W Ltd's European sites and businesses.

The specially built, liquid phosphorus carrying ships – the *Albright Pioneer* and the *Albright Explorer* – made their last voyages from Canada during 1989. The purified wet acid route to food grade phosphoric acid developed at Whitehaven had superseded the phosphorus route, making production of phosphorus at Long Island, Newfoundland, a non-viable operation – the very thing Frank Schon had predicted before his resignation at the start of the Canadian project twenty years earlier.

The USSR

The week 10–17 May 1958 proved to be a significant one for Marchon when a party of technical experts from the USSR spent the whole time in serious discussions with the relevant Marchon personnel. The Russian party included Mssrs Denisov, Karminsky, Antenov, Blagadivov and Mrs Kumleva with the party under the overall control of Mr Naumenko, the Minister of the State Committee for Food. Marchon participants in the discussions included: Frank Schon, Otto Secher, Bob Dickie, Danny Dine, Mike Dufaye, Reg Fell, Brian Milling, Albert Taylor and Dr Adolf Koebner.

Marchon were already selling considerable quantities of finished shampoos and detergents as well as fatty alcohols to the USSR. The purpose of the visit was to see how the USSR could reduce its dependence on imported goods and save their valuable dollars and pounds for more essential purposes. At the time there was no official currency exchange between the two sides of the iron curtain and so trade was very difficult. Rather than risk losing the business altogether Marchon agreed to provide the know-how for the manufacture of methyl esters, alkylolamides and fatty alcohols and build and commission two factories, one at Volgodonsk (near Rostov-on-Don) and another at Shebekino (near Kharkov).

Marchon Italiana's plant at Frosinone near Rome. This new establishment was called Marchon Sud and increased the company's sphere of influence within Europe.

It took a long time between the signing of the contracts on 6 October 1960 and the completion of the construction work in 1963/64. Marchon appointed constructors John Brown Ltd as the main contractor, whilst their own chemical engineering department was heavily involved in the preliminary design work with Gordon Atkinson doing most of the liaison work with C.J.B. Reg Fell spent a great deal of his time working with Russian government officials and I joined the team in 1962 to ensure that the final construction took account of the practical requirements of running the plants and that air, sample and steam points were located in the best possible places. I was also tasked with checking the instruction manuals for all the different processes and for overseeing the training of key Russian personnel in Whitehaven.

Chemical engineer Alan Birkett and I started the pre-commissioning at Volgodonsk in early September 1963. The main party of Marchon personnel arrived in November for the start up, which was completed by the end of February 1964 but not without considerable difficulties.

Everyone then moved on to Shebekino except for the writer; I remained to oversee the final guarantee runs on all the plants and in July moved to Shebekino to complete the same task there, afterwards holding responsibility for all guarantee problems at both sites until 1965.

Marchon personnel involved in the USSR were: John Bainbridge Alan Birkett, David Conner (Shebekino only), Reg Fell, Ron Fogg, Cyril Gordon, Jimmy Martin, Jimmy Mitchell, Martin Rowe, Alan Routledge, Ernie Sanderson, Bill Telford, Eddie Thompson, Tom Thornton (Volgodonsk only) and Geof Waite.

Whilst expansion into Europe was understandable, particularly when the UK were not part of the EEC, because it gave the company a legal trading position, the plants at Castiglione and St Mihiel really should have been enough to meet the European customers needs. When additional plants were opened, they inevitably took away business, production and jobs from Whitehaven.

With the advent of Tenneco further overseas plants were built, particularly in the USA and Canada, some of which used Marchon technology and know-how. Where this occurred and the customer base moved away from Whitehaven, profits in the UK were hit and once Tenneco deserted the ship, the writing was on the wall for the end of the Whitehaven site.

The tank farm and blending plant at Marchon France's factory at St Mihiel (to the north of Paris).

A general view of the headquarters and manufacturing facilities of Marchon France at St Mihiel.

Left: Mike Dufaye, managing director of Marchon France and a former sales director of Marchon Products Ltd, at Whitehaven.

Below: Marchon occasionally entertained the civic dignitaries from the European towns where Marchon had factories. At Whitehaven, Peter Baines welcomes Mrs Teresa Bossini, Concillo Botturi, Guisippi Botturi and the daughter of the mayor of Castiglione.

Frank Schon (extreme left) on his first visit to Russia in 1958. Third from the left in the back row is Alex Lindsay with Reg Fell on the right. Russian personnel included P Naumenko (Minister for Food), N.V. Antanov (from the State Committee for the Chemical Industry) and Madame Mankovskaja.

Marchon tended to set up its European factories using technical and engineering staff from Whitehaven, which in the case of Marchon France included: Terry Palmer, Roy Harrison, Tom Connelly, David and Howard Conner and Mike Fearfield. The company's policy was to slowly hand over key management positions to local people such as Piere Lahalle Gravier.

The Russian specialists expressed a wish to see how oxygen was bottled, so they were taken to the British Oxygen bottling plant at Carlisle in 1963. BOC are world experts on the subject of oxygen and agreed with the Marchon experts that it could not be done safely using oxygen from the electrolysis process because the gas was too reactive. Nevertheless, despite advice to the contrary, they went ahead and built a bottling plant at Volgodonsk which was totally destroyed in a cloud of white smoke when the plant was started up!

Part of the Russian project required that key Russian personnel were trained up in Whitehaven. That responsibility fell to Alan Routledge who is seen here with V.P. Tyagoon, Madame Kostikova, L. Volkov, G. Friedberg and N. Kostikov.

eight

The Final Years
1990–2005

The cessation of production at the Whitehaven works became inevitable during this period, especially after pressure from environmentalists forced the company to stop manufacturing phosphoric acid on site. The knock-on effect of this was the end of the manufacture of sulphuric acid at Solway and the virtual closure of Whitehaven harbour to commercial shipping, all of which were attended by job losses. This final chapter chronicles the slow and painful path, taken by the various owners of the company up to the announcement by Huntsman that all production would cease by June 2005 and the factory finally close for good.

Organics

The Eltersol plant, one of the oldest production units on the Marchon site, finally closed down on 19 July 1991. Both Marchon Italiana and Marchon France had spare capacity and the business was given to them. Whitehaven site Manager Ray Cranke said 'there was no profitable future for this small plant.'

At the same time a new dust extraction system was installed at S5 building to reduce the amount of surfactant being lost, as dust, from the Scott and Niro driers. A spokesman said 'The system cost £400,000 to install and should stop problems with the dust settling on nearby houses. These measures are further steps in improving the environmental standards of the factory.' At the same time a new £3 million boiler house was commissioned well away from the housing estate.

The waste water treatment lagoon, which had been built in the old phosphate rock store, was about 8ft deep and held millions of gallons of waste water awaiting treatment.

The lagoon allowed drainage water to be treated with bacteria which broke down any surfactant material which may have been present in the water. The surfactant materials came from spillages or leaks which found their way into the drainage system. After treatment the waste water was discharged into the sea, resulting in much fewer problems with foam.

As part of the general push towards a better environment during 1992, the large redundant phosphate rock store, known locally as the cathedral, was converted into a covered lagoon for holding waste water until any surfactant it contained was reduced. Thus the unsightly foam slicks formed on the surface of the sea were eliminated. The cost of the scheme was £0.5 million.

Inorganics

During the summer of 1991, the company announced:

Breakthrough at Whitehaven on heavy metal extraction. After several years of research it was hoped that the Marchon site will reduce its discharges of heavy metals to the sea by at least 90 per cent.' Works technical manager Howard Connor said 'We hope to be fully geared to the new EC targets for heavy metals, which comes into force in 1995.' Greenpeace spokesman, Christopher Talbot noted 'If it is good as they say, then its very good news indeed.

Marchon was the subject of a private prosecution, brought by Greenpeace, under the Water Act of 1989, and Whitehaven Magistrates found them guilty of discharging an amount of toxic effluent into the sea which exceeded the consent levels permitted by the National Rivers

The outflow pipes from the lagoon to the sea. The discharge was continuously analysed to ensure that all the requirements of the various water and health and safety authorities were met.

Authority. Although the company contested the case, they were fined £2,000 and ordered to meet the £20,000 costs of Greenpeace. Just a few days later, jubilant Greenpeace divers blocked the Marchon outflow pipe in a vain attempt to close the works down.

It proved a costly exercise for Greenpeace when five women and eighteen men were remanded on bail to appear in court at a later date. Works director John Markham said 'The raid was a disgrace, it was premeditated vandalism, putting operators and equipment at risk as well as the Greenpeace divers themselves. They just want to close the factory down which would lead to the loss of 1,500 jobs.' Later Greenpeace were fined heavily and all the defendants were banned from going near the Whitehaven works. Nevertheless Marchon closed the phosphoric production unit down within a year, thereby stopping the main cause of effluent from the plant.

Phosphoric acid production from imported phosphate rock ceased in 1992 after thirty-eight years of continuous operation, leading to a great reduction in the requirement for sulphuric acid within the works. The shut down of most of the sulphuric acid plant followed. This action meant a big reduction in gaseous effluent from the Solway chimney and although management claimed the reasons for the shut downs were economic, there can be no doubt that the need to get on side, environmentally speaking, played a major role in the outcome.

At the beginning of 1992, a new £2 million project to reduce heavy metal discharges was well under way. Research at Whitehaven led to the discovery that neutralising the acid effluent with quick lime produced a solid material in which the heavy metals were permanently sealed.

The £2.6 million heavy metals treatment plant came on stream on time and without any overspends. The Rafinate Plant, as it was called, was fully commissioned by the end of June

The outflow pipe at full stream onto the beach at Barrowmouth. The outflow pipe was covered by the sea for most of the day and only became visible at low tide. This pipe was finally blocked by Greenpeace protesters after several attempts.

1992 and Marchon's phosphoric acid requirements were met by importing the acid direct from Morocco through Workington docks. The Moroccan acid still contained the same heavy metal impurities as those produced at Whitehaven and required treatment in the new Rafinate plant. Originally it was hoped that the rock-like material, in which the heavy metals were trapped, would be used as aggregate in construction work but the cost of transport of the cheap material meant it was un-saleable and had to be stockpiled on site. All these changes meant job losses and redundancies. The Rafinate plant was opened officially by the Right Honourable Michael Howard QC MP, the Secretary of State for the Environment, on 9 March 1992.

Management

The period opened with a flurry of senior staff retirements from Whitehaven, all after long years of service with the company. Bill Adair, commercial director of A&W Ltd, retired during 1991 after twenty-eight years of service. Bill, who started as a senior assistant chemist in the Marchon technical service department, moved to sales and by 1969 was export sales manager for Africa. From there he rose steadily through the ranks to reach director level in January 1986.

Several managers based at Whitehaven, including works technical manager Howard Connor, public relations manager Mike Clay, and distribution manager Terry Ponting, left the company after twenty-five, thirty-one and twenty-three years respectively.

These were followed by process control group manager, Mike Crosby (forty-three years); area manager, Colin Jackson (thirty-five years); engineering admin manager, Tom Sowerby (thirty-three years); and production managers, Brian Harper (thirty years) and John Douglas (twenty-nine years). Close on their heels came phosphates area manager, Don Baxter (forty-two years) and analytical services manager, Hugh Fletcher (forty years). There were a further thirty-seven retirements during 1992.

Management at Marchon were in trouble again in October 1993 over discharges to the sea from a geological fault situated half a mile away from the plant. The National Rivers Authority warned the company that 'the accidental leaks must be stopped by the end of June 1993 or there would be a prosecution.' In reply, the company said 'We have put in as much effort and detailed investigation as is possible to try to locate and then stop the leak. We have so far spent £450,000 on checking all the main pipelines and will spend a further £150,000 by the end of the year.'

In an attempt to make better use (financially speaking) of the company's plants and assets, A&W introduced a number of asset management teams with the aim of doubling the company's profits by 1999, without spending money on the plants themselves. The profit improvement teams added $5 million to the company's balance sheet in 1993. Their main efforts were directed at coaxing extra production from plants already working at capacity, rather than spend money on upgrades and repairs. This action would never prolong the life of the production units.

The A&W annual report for 1994 was quoted in US$ and the chairman noted 'some hopeful signs'. According to the report the company had made a trading profit, for the half year, of $29.9 million on a turnover of $463.7 million after deducting $7 million for the restructuring of the Whitehaven site.

Ever since taking over A&W, Tenneco Inc had produced much greater profit margins worldwide than in the UK, leaving their American shareholders unhappy with the state of affairs at A&W Ltd. Despite the neverending round of management changes things only got worse and it came as no surprise when, in 1995, Tenneco said enough was enough and sold the company back to its directors. Once again A&W were floated on the UK stock market, opening at 192p per share on 1 August 1995. By 30 October their value had fallen to 159p. The chief executive, Robin Paul said 'We need to expand our purified acid capacity and drive our growth in specialities and above all reshape our surfactants business.' He added that A&W were looking to invest in Mexico and emphasised 'the revitalisation of our surfactants will not fail for lack of decisive management.'

Part of the new chairman Sir Christopher Benson's management style was to strive for a consensus; if necessary waiting until everyone concerned with a particular topic had all the time they wanted to reach a decision with which they all agreed. He is on record as stating 'if you can make the vote unanimous, then everyone is party to the decision' – a long way from Robin Paul's decisive management.

The summer of 1996 brought more tinkering to management when the Phosphates and Surfactants Group was 'streamlined and focused'. Two general sales managers were appointed under the direction of Ian Black – John Brown for phosphates and David Connor for detergents and surfactants.

During the spring of 1996 Whitehaven site manager, Ray Crank said:

As A&W Ltd move into the last five years of the twentieth century, it is harnessing two major programmes to improve its performance and to retain its place in the vanguard of management practices. The first of these is operating cost leadership, which will continue to be vital in developing a leaner, athletic and competitive organisation of world class. The second is involvement, which can be over-simplified by contrasting the old days with today. Then decisions were made by management and the workforce carried them out. Today we recognise that all workers have ideas as to how the company should be run and would like to play a greater part in the company's future.

The concrete foundations for the Solway kilns were so big that it took several years to clear the site after the kilns became redundant.

A demolition job of this scale produced mountains of debris of all kinds and required the constant use of heavy lifting gear.

The actual size of the kilns can be gauged from this photograph. Constructed from steel an inch thick and lined with heavy refractory bricks, their dismantling was no easy task, even for specialist demolition companies.

Rik Gilbert replaced Ray as site manager but did not last long before Ian Woodhouse, the former European buying manager, replaced him with effect from 1 March 1999.

Towards the end of 1998 the American company Albermarle offered 130p per share for all of A&W's shares. Hot on their heels were ISPG with an offer of 145p per share. Albermarle was a global supplier of speciality chemicals and intermediates and was established in 1887 becoming a publicly traded company in 1994 employing 2,700 people worldwide.

ISPG Plc was formed by the privately owned Austrian company Donau Chemie AG for the sole purpose of making a bid for A&W Ltd. To complicate the issue even further, Rhodia had an option to purchase ISPG any time after 1 January 2000. Paris-based Rhodia is a speciality chemicals company formed in 1998 by Rhone–Poulenc and employs 26,000 people worldwide.

Albermarle's offer of 130p per share valued the company at £408 million and the directors felt that the chances of A&W shares reaching anywhere near that figure on the UK stock market were zero. They then announced that they were in favour of Albermarle's offer and advised the shareholders accordingly.

ISPG's offer of 145p per share, made on 16 March 1999, put the company's value at £445 million and while negotiations continued A&W refused to make any further comment. While the uncertainty continued, management changes were again the order of the day. Whitehaven

The kilns were cut up into sections for easier handling and to allow the fire brick lining to be removed before the kiln shells were cut up for scrap.

Sale correspondent, Tom McGrady, discusses a new product data sheet with technical sales manager Tom Smith. Product data sheets were distributed by the sales staff to potential customers and were constantly reviewed and updated.

site manager Ian Woodhouse announced those changes at the works which would come into effect from 1 August 1999. A total of thirty-five day managers were involved and when the changes were complete the Whitehaven site had a total of over forty day staff, out of a workforce of 700, with manager in their job title.

Following a very complex series of deals, Rhodia finally purchased A&W Ltd in 2000 and immediately began to move production to their French sites, steadily closing down much of the Whitehaven site. With each section closure came a batch of redundancies with the workforce down to 500 by April 2000 and just 300 by August.

Rhodia soon sold the detergents and surfactants business to Huntsman Surface Sciences, of Salt Lake City, who promised a much better future for the Whitehaven site. The deal between Rhodia and Huntsman was not quite what it seemed; Huntsman only purchased the goodwill and customer base for surfactants business and only leased the plant from Rhodia. When Rhodia finally closed the phosphates plant in 2002 and started to dismantle all the unused part of the factory during 2003, there were just 150 people left working on the site

Between 2002 and 2004 Huntsman made a number of promises to the workforce about investments in Whitehaven, including a promise of £11 million to secure the future of the site and safeguard the remaining eighty-two jobs. This announcement was made in June 2004. Just six months later the workforce were given an unpleasant Christmas present – notice of the closure of the works by June 2005. Little, if any, of the promised millions had been spent.

The lime hopper at the Rafinate plant, in which impurities in the phosphoric acid were converted to a harmless solid aggregate by treatment with lime.

Marchon's experience, at the hands of American masters, has been one of uncertainty and these companies clearly had only one loyalty – to their American shareholders. They were totally indifferent to the welfare of the community which would be seriously effected by their actions and, like Rhodia before them, Huntsman moved production to their other sites taking the customer base with them, without which the site had no chance of recovery.

Lastly, I dedicate this book to everyone who has worked at Marchon over the past sixty years or so, especially those friends and colleagues who worked with me during my thirty years at Marchon.

Above: The new amine plant was built in 1977 and survived the takeover of A&W Ltd by Rhodia. It was part of the deal between Huntsman and Rhodia but eventually closed down during 2005.

Right: Part of the purified phosphoric acid plant, which produced food grade acid used in the manufacture of Coca Cola, among many other food products. Rhodia moved all the business from this plant to France in 2002 and closed and demolished the plant.

Opposite above: A rotary kiln was the final stage of the heavy metals entrapment process on the Rafinate plant.

Opposite below: The jet engine housing and steam raising plant at the combined power plant, jointly operated by A&W Ltd and Powergen. Any electricity surplus to the factories needs was sold to the national grid. The plant used two Rolls-Royce Avon jet engines burning natural gas to produce both electricity and steam.

The STPP plants were, for many years, a major landmark at the Marchon site. After Rhodia took over, the plants were quickly closed and became a sorry sight.

A final look at a once great factory. The photograph includes most of the works from S4 on the left to Solway on the right. After employing 2,500 people, at the time this photograph was taken in the 1970s, the site now employs a handful of demolition workers.